T3-BOE-339

DUKE UNIVERSITY PUBLICATIONS

One and Twenty

One and Twenty

Duke Narrative and Verse

1924-1945

Selected by WILLIAM BLACKBURN

Designed and Illustrated
by pupils of
CLARE LEIGHTON

DUKE UNIVERSITY PRESS

1945

PRINTED IN THE UNITED STATES OF AMERICA
BY THE SEEMAN PRINTERY, INC., DURHAM, N. C.

FOR MEMBERS OF ENGLISH 103
PAST AND PRESENT

Foreword

Clare Leighton, the English wood engraver, has just completed a two-year stay on the campus as a visiting lecturer in art, and this book is one of her inspirations. In the spring of 1944 she was planning a course in the art of the book and wanted fresh material on which her pupils could work. Would I be interested in getting up a volume of student material? It seemed a fine idea. But in mulling it over I decided to expand the notion somewhat by mixing the writings of both undergraduates and graduates—using "graduates" in a very loose sense of the word. Such a collection, it appeared, might suggest an answer to the perennial question as to when amateur writing becomes professional; it would give the current generation of undergraduate writers something to aim at; it might reflect a little deserved glory on our writers themselves. Since time was short and the fifty-eight volumes of the *Archive* (the oldest college lit. in the South, I believe the saying is) seemed too arduous a research, I chose the year 1924, the year in which the University was founded, as the outer limit of my exploration. After reading twenty-one years of Duke writing, I pitched upon ONE AND TWENTY, a phrase from Housman's famous poem, as a title. Its implication of youth, I must confess, has not met with universal approval, as some of our contributors are well beyond the metaphorical two-and-twenty. I beg their indulgence.

Should the gentle reader ask for a point of view from which he may read this anthology, perhaps I could do no better than to pass on a remark of one of our poets: "If you care to look into the file of such-and-such a magazine," he says, "I know you will find one poem of mine which I regard as respectable, though not as great as Chaucer." That has often seemed to me the perfect touchstone for the college anthologist. Nor have I been unmindful of the warning Robert Frost, in describing the difficulty of breaking into professional print, recently gave a group of Duke students: "Your teacher is paid to love you; an editor is paid to hate you." I hope I have been sufficiently "editorial."

I am obliged to many people for their help. First of all I should like to thank the alumni, faculty, and students, whose faith and subscriptions made possible the publication of this book. I mention with particular gratitude the support given me by Mr. Charles A. Dukes, of the Public Relations Office; by Miss Anne Garrard, Alumni Secretary; by Mr. Albert Wilkinson and Mrs. Lucille K. Boyden of the News Bureau; by Mr. W. T. Laprade, Director of the Press; and by three undergraduates who served as chairmen of subscription committees: Mr. William Brinkley, Miss Barbara Taeusch, and Miss Jane Meriwether.

If it is possible to praise the editorial wisdom of my friend Mr. Ashbel Brice without seeming to saddle him with editorial responsibility, I want to say the volume is very much better for his having gone over the manuscript with me. Mr. E. D. Fowler of the Seeman Printery has given me the benefit of his special wisdom in seeing the book through the press.

Mrs. William McDougall has done the University community a great kindness in allowing me to print a selection from the letters of the late Lieutenant Kenneth Dougal McDougall.

I must mention finally my indebtedness to various publishers for their kind permission to reprint the following copyright material:

The American Mercury: Julian Lee Rayford's "Two Alabama Wildcats" (April, 1939).

Charm: Mary Gus Rodgers's "'To the Wilderness Dead'" (March, 1945).

Coronet: Archie Robertson's "Our Little Trains" (November, 1944).

Esquire: David Cornel DeJong's "Calves" (August, 1939).

Harper and Brothers: "Question" and "In Memoriam" from David Cornel DeJong's *Across the Board* (1943).

Harper's Magazine: John Schaffner's "Winter Sunset" (November, 1941).

The Kenyon Review: Frances Gray Patton's "A Piece of Bread" (Autumn, 1944).

Alfred A. Knopf, Inc.: "The Freight Train," "That Beauty Passes Like a Dream," "Confederate," "Watching Children," "For H. W. W.," from George Zabriskie's *The Mind's Geography* (1941).

———: a chapter from Richard Austin Smith's *The Sun Dial* (1942).

Curtis Publishing Company: Opal Winstead's "Gray Street" in the *Saturday Evening Post* (February 8, 1941).

The Saturday Review of Literature: John Schaffner's "Golden Gazelle" (September 12, 1936), and his "On Southern Station" (December 9, 1944).

———: Frances Gray Patton's "In Common with the Earth" (August 4, 1945).

Scribner's Magazine: Julian Lee Rayford's "A Certain Seclusion" (June, 1939).

Southwest Review: Ovid Williams Pierce's "One of the Darkies" (Winter, 1942).

Story: R. P. Harriss's "Red Coat Day" (May, 1935).

Tomorrow: John Schaffner's "A Country Boy" (June, 1944).

Virginia Quarterly Review: R. P. Harriss's "Autumnal: Carolina Low Country" (October, 1928).

William Blackburn.

Duke University
August, 1945

Contents

One and Twenty

Letters from the Front

Kenneth Dougal McDougall

Co. B., 7th Bn., 1st Repl. Depot,
["Somewhere in North Africa,"]
November 13th, 1943

DEAR MUM,

. . . I was walking on my little mountain the other day when I came upon a pile of knobbly roots that had been dug out of the ground. I picked out a good one and started whittling. It was the root of a scrub oak tree that grows here, with big acorns and prickly leaves like holly.

Presently an old Arab came trudging up the trail, leading a tiny donkey with immense basket panniers on its sides. We conversed in pidgin French-Italian and sign language, but I couldn't make out what he was going to do with the roots, which he started to pile into the panniers. All he would say was "centi, centi, hundle, hundle," meaning "a hundred." When I still shook my head he gathered up a hundred pebbles and counted them off in Arabic. Thinking he might be asking money for the piece of wood I had taken, I gave him a quarter. He looked it over, bit it, bounced it on a rock, and beamed all over. He apparently wanted to give me his entire farm, donkey and all. Finally, we sealed the bargain with a pinch of "Granger," and I made off with my root.

I whittled away nights and finally produced another spoon, which I am sending you. The design is an Arabic one that I saw in a museum here. Also in the package (if you ever get it) is a little stone buckle that I made for P. Y. Please send it on to her if she is no longer with you.

.... My training at present is chiefly physical. We start each day with an hour of calisthenics and usually have a good march or run to follow. Sometimes we go down the cliffs to the sea and climb up again. You can imagine how that suits me. There are wonderful red, brown, and purple sea anemones among the rocks, sea urchins, sea cucumbers, starfish, hermit crabs, and *barnacles.* It is astonishing that most of my companions never see such things at all. Those who do are often afraid of them, or frankly incurious. I shall always be grateful for my broad scientific education. It enables me to see and enjoy a host of things that most people are not even aware of.

.... I am still anxiously awaiting your mail, but it may be a couple of weeks yet before it starts coming through.

Ever your loving and affectionate son

Kenneth

Co. A, 30th Repl. Bn.,
7th Repl. Depot,
November 27th, 1943

Dear Mum,

Notice the new address. Still "somewhere in North Africa," but several days' train ride from the last place. . . .

Train travel in this country is not exactly luxurious. You may remember hearing of the famous French "40 and 8" box cars that were so much used in the last war. Forty men or eight horses. Well, they all seem to have wound up here. The mystery is how the French managed to get forty men into one of them. We pack twenty-nine men and one officer, and when they are all lying down at night, there is a good deal of overlapping. We are provided with "C" rations, the U. S. Army canned food. It is good stuff, even when you must eat it cold, as so often happens. Drinking water is always a problem, of course, and so is "plumbing." The most trying thing, though, is the French system of operating rail traffic. The trains actually spend about one third of the time standing still, for no apparent reason, and are not exactly speeding during the other two thirds. At every stop the men pile off onto the tracks to stretch their legs, relieve themselves, bargain with the Arabs, or buy what is to be had in the French canteens. Often we have time to light fires on the tracks and heat our food. All of a sudden the whistle blows and the train starts to move. Men come running from every direction, pulling up their pants, stuffing sandwiches into their pockets, grabbing their ration cans off the fire, and tumble into the train head over heels. Then, maybe, it is a false alarm, and we all pile out again to repeat the performance a few minutes, or a few hours, later. Believe me, it is a nerve-racking business to see that none of one's men gets left behind. . . .

The rainy season is here and no mistake. Our beautiful hillside is a slithery mass of mud that seems to get deeper every day. This tent is dug into the hillside to make the floor more or less level. We arrived at night, in the rain, and floundered in here by the light of a candle. Since then we have dug trenches, built steps, gathered stones for the floor, and generally made ourselves as comfortable as possible. It is not at all bad, but I still can't help thinking of *Journey's End* when we light our little candle at night.

We arrived here just in time for the Thanksgiving dinner that we had so long been anticipating. It was good, too. Turkey and all the "fixin's." I have just finished censoring about eight hundred letters, and I don't think there was one that failed to mention the turkey.

The further we go, the "tougher" it gets, but you know I don't mind *physical* hardships. As a matter of fact, it will have to get a whole lot tougher to equal some of the times I went through in Scotland!

I wonder how you liked my little poem. It was so long since I have written one that it was quite a surprise to find it coming. If I could only get off by myself more often, I might be able to write more.

With all good wishes for Christmas and 1944,

Your loving son

Kenneth.

Headquarters 5th Army,
G-3 Training Section,
["Somewhere in Italy,"]
January 3rd, 1944

Dear Mum,

. . . It is becoming extremely difficult to concentrate on this letter. You see, my little landlord and his wife are literally smothering us with kind attentions. They have just persuaded me to sit with them this evening, so that the pan of red hot charcoal under the table can warm all of us at once. It is an economical arrangement; the trouble is that neither of them has a word of English, yet both insist upon talking to me all the time. At this moment he is thumbing through an ancient Italian grammar, cooking up some further wise remarks for my attention. Nothing can stop him. Yesterday we could not refuse to eat lunch with them—at 3:00 P.M., just after a substantial G.I. lunch! We made heroic attempts to swallow what passes with them for food, but had to give up in the end. The wine went very well, though. (Well, he has just got it out. It seems he wants to take me to see the doctor's daughter, who is to act as interpreter between us! Then he'll really go to town!)

This house clings to the side of a mountain like a mud-wasp's nest stuck to a wall. It is as cold as a tomb and just as stony. However, it is clean, and the sun shines brightly. Our room has a little porch boiling over with potted pink geraniums, from which we have a fine view over the town and the surrounding country.

Today four of us toiled up to a monastery that is stuck on a ledge about a thousand feet above the town. There was snow on the ground up there—it seemed like another world entirely, so quiet and still. A young Franciscan monk showed us around, not forgetting to demonstrate a sacred drop of blood in a little bottle. The war surged by this place, but I shouldn't wonder if these monks were not even aware of it.

When we started down again the monk came with us. It seemed he was taking a donkey and a pig down to the market. At first the donkey started off bravely, but the pig absolutely refused to head down hill. It was just about as strong as the monk, so their tug-of-war was a tie. Then an idiot boy came up and started beating the pig with a stick. With ear-splitting squeals the pig took off like a shot from a gun, the monk tearing along behind on the other end of the string, his brown robes flying. They soon overtook us and the donkey too. At this point the donkey decided to turn round and go back. We persuaded him against it with some trouble, and finally the monk got hold of both his animals at once. With a stroke of something very like genius, he tied them to opposite ends of the same string, pig leading, donkey in the rear, and monk in the middle, throwing his weight this way or that according to the needs of the moment. In this way they got along famously, except that the pig objected to corners and tried to take a short cut for home at every turn in the trail. Here and there we passed a peasant woman gathering wood, each of whom would deliver a good whack on one of the three, whichever happened to be within range. Things went at a great rate till near the bottom of the hill, when the procession ran into six cows, two goats, two dogs, and a boy. I didn't think any of us would come out of that alive. However, when the yelling and squealing died away, the cattle were scattered to the four winds; and the pig, the monk, and the donkey were still on their way to market in good order. I never did find out what happened to the idiot boy. We all laughed so much we could hardly get home. I just wish you could have seen it all.

This letter will be getting overweight pretty soon, so more later.

Your loving son

Kenneth

Headquarters 5th Army,
Mountain Warfare Training Team,
["Somewhere in Italy,"]
January 30th, 1944

Dear Mum,

. . . We have been having a slack time lately and enjoying ourselves in a big way. I took off one day to explore a great gorge, or canyon, not far away. It is about a thousand feet deep and several miles long. It was quite a job getting down into it by following goat tracks down the cliffs. At the bottom a small stream rushed along between towering rock walls. At places the cliffs almost met overhead, shutting out the daylight, and it was like the "caverns measureless to man" where "Alph the sacred river ran." Here and there a side gorge opened into it, and a zig-zag trail wound steeply up to pastures on the high slopes.

As I made my way down stream, the gorge opened out into a narrow green valley with sheep and goats grazing in it. Purple crocuses were in bloom everywhere, and hazel catkins were already long and yellow.

Presently there came a shout that echoed back and forth from the cliffs on either side: *"Where Are You Going, Johnny?"* All I could see was an immense pile of brush moving along on two very short human legs. It turned out to be a little old man, little more than a dwarf. When he dropped his load, I saw two twinkly black eyes, a huge hooked nose, rosy red cheeks, and a fuzz of yellow beard. He continued to speak in a voice that seemed to shake the very mountains. He had lived in New York for twelve years but was already forgetting the language; so much of his shouting was of no avail. I made out that he was seventy-four years old, and, like everyone else hereabouts, intends to return to the States after the war. I left him shouting at his sheep and feeding them the brush that he had carried down the cliff for them.

. . . . Thank you for your reply to my cablegram. Now I know that you were alive and well last November!

Your loving son

Kenneth

Hq. 1st Special Service Force,
["Somewhere in Italy"]
March 14th, '44

Dear Mum,

. . . I shall not pretend to you that this present job is perfectly safe. It isn't. On the other hand, it is probably a good deal less dangerous, and less uncomfortable too, than you imagine. It is still true that "war," as somebody said, "is mostly waiting." Even when there is a sharp engagement with many casualties, it always turns out that most of the casualties are merely wounded, and many of those are back on the job after a few weeks in hospital. Being wounded is not nearly such a serious matter as it used to be.

I tell you these things because I myself am just beginning to realize their truth and significance. The picture one gets of war from books, newspapers, and even from first-hand accounts, is surprisingly false. The reason is that the incidents people talk and write about are naturally the exciting incidents that make good reading. All the humdrum, day-to-day living in between them is just not interesting enough to be mentioned. And yet *most* of our days are humdrum. For any one man a battle is the exception rather than the rule. You would be surprised to know how many men get bored with the daily routine and actually look forward to some "action," as they call it, with enthusiasm. Everyone would prefer to go home, of course, but since we must be here it is better to be actively engaged than just sitting about and waiting.

Our company inhabits a long earth bank on the edge of a field. It is just like a prairie-dog colony. I stick my head out in the morning and see other heads pop up all down the row. One by one we come out into the open, stretch, walk about a bit, look at the sky. Presently smoke goes up everywhere and the smell of breakfast drifts across the field. We do exercises, problems of one sort or another, clean our equipment, improve our dugouts, play football or baseball sometimes.

Every now and then there is a loud BANG! as one of Jerry's shells goes overhead. He is not shooting at us, so no one even looks up. Sometimes we can see a great fountain of earth and smoke where the shell hits. More often the shells come over one horizon and disappear over the other with nothing to be seen. They are none of our business.

On fine days such as we have been having lately, time

goes quite quickly. I noticed that the grass is distinctly greener and longer each day. There are some wild lark-spur with tight-packed flower buds, just turning blue in the last two days. They should be out next week. I watch the daisies open up each morning and close again at night. The birds act as if they had nesting matters in mind.

At dusk, if there is no job on hand, we crawl back into our holes, cover the opening tight, and light up the candles for an hour or so of reading or talking. Sometime during the night there is sure to be a Jerry plane about, taking pictures, or dropping a bomb or two. He doesn't dare to come over in daylight. We seldom see him, but the guns roar from every hedgerow. They made a wonderful sound. Quick-firing A.A. guns go "room, room, room, room" till the very air seems to be rumbling, on and on. If the plane comes lower, machine guns start barking out: "Ack, ack, ack," in quick succession, dozens of them at once. Red tracer bullets go arching into the sky in long, flat, graceful curves. Shell bursts wink like huge red sparks among the stars. Then suddenly it all stops and there is dead silence, save for the earth-shaking rumble and distant flashing of big guns far away.

I told you once before how big shells passing overhead make a whispering sound, like the rustle of birds' wings. There are others, high velocity shells, that pass over with a loud "BANG!" followed by a resonant booming sound, like someone drumming on an empty water butt. On a still night the booming seems to echo from all sides, as if the sky were an immense dome of glass that someone had struck from the outside. After this has died away comes the sound of the exploding shell, sharp and far away.

I was out in no-man's-land with a patrol one night,

looking for certain information. We were like a lot of thugs sneaking along the hedgerows in the moonlight. We had blackened our hands and faces, wore our oldest clothes, and carried rifles, knives, and hand-grenades in our pockets. Quite suddenly we were fired on by a machine gun near a house, quite close. One man was shot in the leg. We ducked behind a bank, and another gun opened up from that side. A flare went up, and we squeezed ourselves against the ground, holding our breath till it burnt out. Mortar shells started to burst around us, the shrapnel whining overhead like angry bees. We scrambled back along the ditch and got away from all that.

We next made a wide detour and started along a ditch across a field. But someone could see us, for shells started coming over "S-S-S-BANG!"—"S-S-S-BANG!" The ditch was full of muddy water, but we got right down in it on our bellies and wriggled away from there like worms on a hot brick.

We went back still farther and tried a detour on the other side. But we were seen again, and mortar shells came crashing down close by. They scared up a whole flock of pewits that flew off in the moonlight, crying their strange cry. Every now and then one of those big shells went "BANG!" overhead and set the sky to rumbling as it whistled away over the horizon. It was all very exciting and strange. I was surprised to find that I was not particularly scared.

Later that night we stalked for miles along the bank of a flooded canal, among pine trees. It was very muddy, and the water in the ditch came well above our knees. There were birds in the marsh, bitterns perhaps, that sounded just like people talking quietly. It stopped us every time, finger on trigger. Once we were stopped like that, crouched, listening, when I saw a man walking towards us in the shadows. We kept still and he came quite close, then stopped, listening, and looking straight at us. For at least a minute there wasn't a sound or a movement. I could think of nothing to say that seemed appropriate. Someone said, "Hands up!" The man put up his hands and said: "I'm English." And he said it in a Scots accent that you could cut with a knife. He had been taken prisoner by the Germans and was coming back through our lines.

Dawn was breaking as we came back. We had been out all night. My feet had *never* been so cold!

We did not get the information we particularly wanted that night, but I, at least, learnt quite a number of things. Among others, the appearance of wild narcissi by moonlight. There were great clumps of them along the canal, sweet scented.

Don't forget what I have told you, that *most* of our days and nights are humdrum. Would you rather I did not write about the exciting moments?

Please give my kindest regards to Suggy, and to Mrs. Smith when you see her. You can tell Miss Baldwin that the field glasses she gave me are extremely useful. I have been using them constantly.

Your loving son

Kenneth

5th Co., 1st Rgt., FSSF,
["Somewhere in Italy,"]
May 2nd, 1944

Good morning! How are you this fine May morning? Are the bluebirds trying to nest yet, or is it to be sparrows and starlings again this year? How are the willows growing? And the hedge?

Your Easter present has just arrived. Once more you have hit the spot in your choice of books. I am delighted with the Voltaire and the French and Italian readers. Thank you.

All is quiet here except for air raids. The "ack-ack" last night was a magnificent display. One of the few beautiful things produced by war.

Your loving son

Kenneth

5th Co., 1st Regt., FSSF,
[Anzio Beachhead,]
May 10th, '44

Dear Mum,

Well, we had it almost cleaned up and fit to live in—and moved again.

This time we dug ourselves holes in the ground to sleep in. It was a lot of hard work, but no one regretted it. There were a couple of air raids last night, and our area was shelled too. I woke up at about midnight. Each explosion made the very earth jump under me. The noise was deafening. As I lay there with my ears ringing and soil shaking down onto my face, I heard a nightingale singing. The explosions must almost have shaken him from his perch, yet he never ceased for a moment.

I had not heard a nightingale since Boar's Hill days, but recognized the song immediately. What a wonderful, varied, serene warbling it is. No wonder that the poets of all ages have found it full of meaning. I found myself weeping at the beauty of it and at all the thoughts of long ago that it revived.

After the infernal racket was over, he kept right on with his song, and then I heard another one answering, far away.

This morning I heard a cuckoo calling, and that too was full of memories. How often I have heard them in the Scottish glens.

Sometimes I despise myself for being a human. No other animal could be so "beastly."

Thank you for sending out additional copies of my thesis. Someday I hope to continue that work, and the criticism of others who are familiar with it will be most valuable.

But for the present it must wait. There is not the slightest chance of my returning to research work until after the war, even if I wished to. Of course, it is a frightful extravagance to risk men, like myself, who have had

many years of expensive training, but war itself is a frightful extravagance.

Anyway, I want to stay here and see what men go through in the battles. You know, front-line troops have a pride in themselves and a hardly concealed scorn for "4-F's" and the "rear echelon" which no one else can really understand. I should not care to be an object of their scorn, either now or after the war. But more than that, it is a chance to find oneself. I don't expect to find Christ in a foxhole, but I am finding out a lot about myself, and about other men.

I am reading *Life and the Poet* in spare moments and find it very interesting.

Your loving son

Kenneth

Anzio Beachhead,
May 17th, 1944

Dear Mum,

We had a hard day yesterday. For hour after hour we worked our way across dusty fields, rushing from one firing position to another. Tanks rumbled by in great clouds of dust. Houses in our path had to be surrounded and attacked one after another. The sun burned down; sweat turned the dust on our bodies and clothes into sticky mud. We waded canals chin deep and tried to run through deep loose sand. It was all by way of training and not a shot was fired, but we were good and tired by 7:00 P.M. when we got back for chow.

At 10:00 o'clock I had to go up to another part of the front line as an observer. Four of us set off in a jeep, careening along in pitchy darkness, without lights. Several times we swerved madly to avoid trucks coming the other way. Holes in the road could not be seen, and the jolts as we crashed over them nearly sent us flying several times. Finally we drew up at a half-ruined house, groped our way through a door hung with blankets, stumbled down some steps, and found three men in a musty cellar, crouched over a candle. A ration party farther down the road would show us the way. So off we went again, on foot this time. Glowing red tracer shells arched into the sky. Green flashes gave us light to see our way. The ration party consisted of three men carrying boxes of food up to a forward position. We followed them across the fields, keeping to the ditches and walking carefully to avoid old mine fields on either side. At last we came to another house and more men crouched round a candle in a crowded little room. All about here there is a horrible smell of decaying cattle and dead Germans, but at this particular spot a long-dead cow in the yard made an almost unbearable stench. Today, as the carcass heats up in the hot sunshine, it is getting worse than ever, and flies swarm in unbelievable numbers.

We spent the remaining few hours of darkness in varying degrees of discomfort. My three companions crept into a narrow space under the floor. I was boosted up onto an old bedspring on top of a pile of sandbags. The spring sloped to one side, and I was in continual danger of rolling off. Large shell holes in the walls let in a cold wind that my one blanket did little to stop. At 4:00 o'clock my teeth were chattering violently.

Suddenly machine guns started chattering, and bullets came cracking past the house. Mortar shells came whining down to crash in the field behind.

It was just starting to get light, and it was necessary for us to get across to the barn to do our observing. The barn is only fifteen feet from the house, but in the day-time there is a German machine gunner who fires at any-one who ventures across. So we gathered behind the house, crossed our fingers, and made a dash for it.

This barn is quite the filthiest place I've seen yet. Literally knee deep in rubbish of every description. Flies swarm everywhere, and already the bugs have gotten under our shirts. We take turns climbing up on a table to look out under a broken tile. With field glasses we can see the German positions, the details of which we came here to search out. It is hard to see much for the tall weeds and the bushes, but they are out there, watching us as we are watching them. We have to crawl past the window on hands and knees, because if he sees us here he will start shelling. As a matter of fact, he has started already. About once a minute a shell whistles over the roof and lands in the field behind. Where will the next one go? Has he seen us? We can only wait and see. The last shell just landed about thirty yards from the house.

While not on watch, I am reading Thornton Wilder's *Bridge of San Luis Rey*. I am wondering whether Brother Juniper was right in his belief that our lives are cut to a pattern and are brought to a close at the appropriate moment. I do not believe it myself, but it makes very little difference anyway. I should be sorry to die now, in this beautiful summer time, but accidents will happen. Instead of "God's will be done," I say, "Let nature take its course." (That last shell was closer than ever!)

May 18th. Well, we came out of that all right and are now back in our own snug little holes. Mine is lined with dead bracken, on which I plan to spend the rest of the morning, catching up on lost sleep. So *au revoir* for the present.

Your loving son

Kenneth

5th Co., 1st Regt., FSSF,
["Somewhere in Italy,"]
May 21st, '44

Dear Mum,

We have just been watching, and hearing, a pipe band of the Seaforth Highlanders. Eighteen bagpipes and three drums. I was so stirred up that I still have goose-pimples all over, just thinking about it. They marched back and forth, back and forth, their kilts and sporrans swinging, sunlight glinting from silver-handled dirks, big boots, hairy knees, bony noses and all. Out in front was a tall, bony, hawk-beaked old Scot, straight as a ramrod, stepping along with a silver-knobbed cane. They looked, and were, as proud as eagles and as tough as nails. They should be too, having taken part in every campaign, including Dunkirk. The music was, as it always is, thrilling, mournful, indomitable. I think all of us who heard it felt stirred.

What a pity it is that the U. S. Army provides nothing more inspiring than a brass band. Instead of encouraging us with martial music, they give us Bing Crosby and Frank Sinatra, slush that merely makes the men homesick. (Croon, swoon, and swing make *me* fighting mad, it's true, but not against the enemy!)

We go into battle thinking of our own skins and how to keep them whole, instead of going out to get the enemy at any cost. I believe a piper here and there would be worth twenty men in any battle.

You have probably heard on the radio that things are beginning to pop around here. Cassino fell yesterday. Don't be surprised if you don't hear from me for a while.

Your loving son

Kenneth

Calves

David Cornel DeJong

"YOU'D think he was crazy. Lugging through all this heat with that water." Mrs. Pierson clamped her mouth shut. The boy went on, lugging two pails up the dead gray hill. A fierce sun stood high above him so that his shadow fell close around his feet. "It won't hurt them calves any," Mrs. Pierson continued, "but he's crazy." She turned to one of her sons. "Where's he got them tied now, Sam?"

"Durn if I know." He shrugged.

"Under the old apple trees. He put them there this morning. I saw him. Pretty near took him an hour, huggin' and pettin' 'em," Margie said. Her words came with a dry intensity as if they were shreds of the heat. She looked wizened and sullen far beyond her thirteen years.

"Well, all I can say he's crazy," Mrs. Pierson barked. She shaded her eyes and studied the whitely glowing sky above the distant Berkshires. Then she turned and went in the house, shooing flies away with her apron. Margie followed. The two sons shouldered mutely into the heat.

The boy had reached the top of the slope. The grass was hard beneath his feet, and grasshoppers whirred up and clanged against the pails. From a clump of trees, crows cawed monotonously.

Underneath the bedraggled apple trees the seven calves were tethered, each to its stake. They had risen when the boy became visible over the slope and were rubbing their heads against the stakes. When he was quite near, they lolled their blue-gray tongues and smacked their lips resoundingly. "Yes, I'm coming," he panted, his voice softening. He had to circle widely around the first three calves to reach the four little bulls, Abner and Tom first. The people back in the house had no names for them. To them they were bulls and calves, brown, black and white. But he had named them. Now they were his; they knew him and needed him.

He set the first pail in front of Abner, a sturdy brown beast, who plunged his blunt head to his eyes in the milky water. "It's an awful day, Abner, boy." The other calves watched Abner's drinking greedily. When Abner was done, he let him suck at the empty pail while he went to Tom with the other pail. He hunched in front of Tom, prattling soft things.

When the pails were empty he trudged back toward the house again to fill them. Behind him he heard the five unappeased calves smack their lips. It made him hurry, in spite of the heat.

He was thirteen, but was much smaller than Margie. Somehow he looked perpetually underfed, especially in the pair of old overalls of his grown cousin. When he had come to the farm last May, they had all poked his ribs and put their fingers in the hollows at his shoulders. "We've got to put weight on him," was their combined verdict. "Maybe we'd better swill him like the hogs," his uncle had grumbled. He had had to look up at his uncle's face to see that it was only a joke. They were all so big and red and healthy. And this farm was going to be his home, all its silently rolling greenness. It had been almost frightening.

His mother was dead. The thought of her had become like a dry hayfield, choking. At the funeral his uncle had said: "Well, I guess there's no other place for you than the farm." He had accepted the inevitable mutely and had gone with his sun-red uncle, not expecting anything, feeling nothing.

After he had been on the farm three days, his oldest cousin had declared that he wasn't good for anything much. He might as well take care of the seven calves, bring them water and skimmed milk, find green places for them. He had not answered, but listened to all the others discuss him, even that girl Margie.

That evening they had brought him to the calves. Before that he had been afraid of the calves, of their clumsy motions, their hard heads. Now his cousins made him come close. They made him hold the pail between his knees while the calves drank. And so he had discovered the large limpid eyes of the calves—which were full of strange reflections and soft shades. That had broken his fear. Those eyes made him think of his mother and things very long ago.

He had had to look up when his cousin was standing

in front of the smallest bull calf, a little black-and-white beast, and said: "If this young idiot don't wanna drink, just kick 'm in the slats." The little beast had sniffed at the watered milk and was backing disconsolately away. "See that?" his cousin had said triumphantly. He gave the calf a resounding kick. "That's the way to treat him."

He had shut his eyes and turned his face. Suddenly he had run away. Behind him his cousin had yelled: "Here, wait, what're you scared of?" Then his cousin had thrust two empty pails into his hands and ordered him to fill them with the diluted milk. But he had already forgotten which of the calves had been fed. It didn't matter. He was going to feed them all over again, in his own way, without kicking them, also without fear for them.

That had been May and now it was August. All the calves knew him; he loved them. They were to him what the family was not. Among his cousins he sat and walked as a stranger. But the summer had turned hot and dry; green places for the calves had become hard to find. He suffered, because he imagined the calves suffered. They would stand taut and expectant whenever he approached them, and then his love for them fused with anguish that soon there would be no more green places for them.

But at the house they called him crazy, because he worried, and because he didn't kick the calves, and because the little black-and-white one had become his pet. Already the second day he had found a way to make the little fellow drink. He had plunged his elbow deep in the whitish water, his fingers extending upward, and the calf had sucked greedily at his fingers, drawing the water up along them, as if he were drinking from an udder. He had named the calf Dicky.

But the heat was great and the drought increased. "He'll get sunstroke, sure as pie," his aunt said about him. "He's crazy," they scolded. All of them, except his uncle, who never scolded and who never spoke kindly to him. But his uncle had the same eyes his mother had had. That made him look long and steadily at his uncle sometimes, who then became uncomfortable and turned his face.

Now it was late August and still the drought remained unbroken. It was early morning. He had just come back from putting the calves beneath the trees before he ate his breakfast. When he entered the house he heard his aunt say: "I don't like butchering at this time of the year. But all my cans are empty, and fresh veal will taste good. And if Mat and Grace want to visit here for a week, all right. He can do the butchering, seeing that's his job in Worcester, and she can help me can the meat."

Her husband had nodded gravely and said: "It's all right by me. It'll save the boys a job, that's sure."

He listened to their conversation. Margie grimaced at him from across the table. When his aunt shoved a bowl of oatmeal in front of him, she said: "There, Joe, how's it seem to you to have three less calves to take care of? The three biggest bulls?" Suddenly he understood. He watched his aunt's red fingers loosen from the bowl and disappear. "How's it seem to you, three less to take care of?" his aunt continued.

But he couldn't even look up. "You see," she went on, "you done such a good job feeding them. They're that nice and fat. And then you won't have to run around in the hot sun a hundred times a day."

At last she was silent, but he realized that they weren't even waiting for his answer. They talked of the butchering. His temples seemed to be pressing together. He looked up in desperation and saw Margie grin meanly at him. He pushed his chair back and ran out of the kitchen. "Eat your oatmeal," his aunt shouted.

"I've got to go," he stuttered, running.

He ran up the hill. The calves had heard the door slam and were waiting to see his head rise above the slope. He stumbled blindly on, his eyes stinging. "Because I made you nice and fat, they're killing you. Because. . . ." He panted and ran on.

When he saw them, he shut his mouth grimly and walked to Abner, the sleekest one, the kindliest one. He laid his forehead between Abner's eyes, against the hard platter of bone. Abner tried to lick his shirt with his long blue tongue. "They're going to kill you, Abner," he sobbed. "Because I put you in the shade." Then he went to Paul and Tom.

While he sat with his forehead against Tom's, he heard footsteps behind him through the dry grass. He turned and saw it was Margie. She came and stood beside him. When Tom tried to butt her, she kicked his wet nose till he staggered back.

"Cut that out," the boy said.

She laughed. "You couldn't eat your oatmeal because these bulls is gonna be butchered," she taunted.

"Go on home," he cried.

"You're a sissy. Crying about them bulls. You're a sissy."

He walked away from her, but she followed him.

"You're a big baby," she continued. "A sissy. You know what my brothers did when they was no bigger than you? I tell you what they done. They butchered a bull calf two weeks old. My brothers did. And they had the old cow standing right there on the other side of the fence. You should have seen that old cow. She got crazy; she yelled, almost like a horse, because she saw them butcher her calf. They're not sissies."

He had come to a stop near the sledge hammer which he used to drive the calves' stakes in the ground. He waited, his eyes fixed only on her feet, his face drawn and bloodless. When she was near, he grabbed the hammer and lifted it. "Shut up. Get out of here. Get out," he shrieked, jumping toward her with the hammer.

Suddenly she ran, shrieking like a maimed fowl. But he did not follow her. He dropped the hammer and walked to an apple tree and pressed his face against the rough stem. "I'm gonna die," he sobbed. "I am going to die."

It was the day before the killing of the calves, and Mat and Grace were coming that evening. For days the skies had threatened rain. Clouds shifted from the Berkshires and rumbled dull thunder. The boy stood against the house, watching his aunt scrub boards in preparation for the killing. His thoughts seemed to have gone to dust; nothing had come of that endless threatening of the sky to prevent the inevitable. Tomorrow they'd be dead.

He watched the uneasy shifting of clouds. He saw them pile higher and at last reach the fierce sun. Thunder growled louder; dragonflies swooped tiredly. "This time we'll get something," his aunt remarked, studying the sky through her tumbled hair. "Just look at that mean sky. I don't like the looks of it."

His lips parted and his breath started coming fast as he watched the awful blackness over the hills. From the fields came the excited yelling of his uncle and cousins and the snorting of horses. But excitedly he watched only the terrible commotion of the clouds. "Come on," he whispered. Unexpectedly the dust whirled up in slow gray spirals and stung his face. Corn blades rustled, stalks creaked, the whole earth seemed to shudder. He licked the dust off his lips, and after a flash of lightning he crooned: "You're coming, coming," in the reverberating volley of thunder. The roaring of the thunder filled everything. From the fields his uncle and cousins came running. Near him his aunt shrieked almost hysterically: "Get in the house, you fool. Are you crazy?"

He looked at her. "No," he shouted, and then he ran away from her into the sudden sheets of rain and hail. He hurled himself up the hill toward the calves, the rain and wind nearly toppling him. The terrible blackness of the sky was churning above tossing trees. He ran. "Ah!" he shouted. He almost flew, flayed by the wind, his clothes plastering against his back, the hail stabbing his neck. "Come on, come on!" he yelled.

Suddenly he was among the calves, their backs hunched to brunt the wind and hail. Then the earth darkened. The blackness had come, and everything bent beneath it. But he stood holding Abner's head and watched the sky. "Come now, come now, quick," he sang. He shut his eyes, but through his closed eyelids he saw the flash of lightning. "Come now and take them all. Take me too. Come, take and kill us, before they do!" he shrieked, opening his eyes toward the sky.

Then he waited, with his arm around Abner's neck. Another flash of lightning nearly blinded him. "See, Abner? See, they're taking us. God, take us."

But the rain and thunder lessened. The corn only

rustled now. With the next volley of thunder he realized it was past, far past. "You're cheating me," he muttered. He pressed Abner's head so hard that the beast tried to wrest himself free. "Don't cheat me," he pleaded.

Then he felt Abner stand still and taut. He thought he felt the earth stand still and taut. There were no sounds, only dripping water, no great sounds, as if everything had fled from the earth. He opened his eyes. He saw the calves stand with heads lowered as if ready to charge. He saw the lividly blue corn against the black sky. He was almost afraid to watch that sky; it was lowering, crouching, as if ready to pounce. The first thunder seemed to be fleeing from it. Out of it rose other thunder with a strange, mad sound, which seemed like that awful blackness become audible. It grew mightier. Abner started to scrape the ground as if he had suddenly grown into a mature bull. "Look, look, look!" he cried to Abner.

He said no more. He tried to grab Abner again, but Abner had grown wild. He saw the house and its pines fade suddenly in gray and white. The thunder slapped and crackled upon the earth as if it were trying to break it apart. "Look!" he shrieked, trying to dodge Abner's charging.

Everything was huge sound and gray blackness. But he did not shut his eyes. The storm had come for him. Fiercer things than thunder. The sounds of God. "The bigness of God!" he shrieked, running among the wild calves. Abner reared and charged, bending the stake to which he was tied. The stake yielded, stood awry as if it jabbed against the thunder, then fell and dragged behind Abner, who galloped in wild circles through the storm.

The boy stood still, blinded by rain, trying to watch Abner. "Abner," he said softly, impotently, realizing he'd never be able to catch Abner again. Abner was part of the storm. The storm had gone into Abner. He stood transfixed while Abner circled around him and nearly toppled him. But suddenly he knew what he was going to do.

He pulled Tom's stake out of the ground, then Paul's. Both hurled after Abner. He ran after them, shrieking, his arms apart. He heard the calves charging around him and then followed him. Paul's stake, still attached to the rope, jangled.

Wildly they charged over the uneven pasture, over oatfields, the calves sometimes ahead, sometimes beside, sometimes charging madly away from him, out of sight, to emerge again out of sound and rain. He did not know where he was running. "Oh, God," he cried. "Oh, God, you've come." He screamed, trying to raise his voice futilely above wind. There was only grayness ahead of him, no land. Once he thought he saw the house, but then suddenly there was a barbed-wire fence and the calves charged through it, and he followed, tearing his clothes, ripping his legs.

The calves were like demons. Below them he saw the river, milling and foaming. "You've come!" he shrieked, unable to stop now. He could no longer hear his own voice. The calves reared beneath him, stopped by a dense snarl of vines behind which the river roared. Paul's stake was caught in the tangles, the other two calves charged Paul, with eyes red and terrible. But the boy wasn't afraid. He was among them. Then Paul broke loose, and all the calves plunged toward the terrible river below them. He jumped after them. Suddenly a powerful hand clutched his shoulder and dragged him back. He didn't cry. He heard his uncle's voice bellow unintelligible things. But the calves tumbled on.

He caught a momentary glimpse of his uncle's face, a face distorted with horror. He struggled to get free. He saw Abner crash through the last tier of bushes; he saw the river whirl blackly and churn over Abner's brown-and-white body. He shrieked. His uncle's hand clutched harder. "Tom!" he cried, for Tom had followed Abner, and Paul was following. The river whirled away with Tom. Tom's head lifted, turning, tumbling. Then Paul was beneath the water. He stopped shrieking. Suddenly he stood rigid and looked up at his uncle. "They're gone," he said.

His uncle pressed him close against him. His uncle's face turned down to him was like something hewn out of red clay. He looked at the river again, but it no longer lifted the calves. He shuddered. He again looked at his uncle's blue frightened eyes and the mouth which was now twisting to a crooked, relieved smile. Then his uncle's strong arm guided him up the slippery bank away from the river. "We're going home," his uncle said.

The storm was ceasing. "You're so wet, you'll get sick," his uncle said, wrapping his own jacket around his shoulders. "You . . ." he was going to continue, but stopped, the blue eyes relieved.

They plodded over the soaked pasture. Nothing mattered now. The three calves were in the river, and this was peace. Suddenly his uncle stopped and lifted him in his arms. He clutched his uncle's red wet neck, while his uncle said: " Don't you ever do that again."

They walked past the four remaining calves, huddled miserably in the rain. They walked past uprooted trees. The house became visible, and from it his aunt and cousins came running toward them. He held on firmer to his uncle's neck. "And don't you ever tell them you loosened them. Tell them they broke loose," his uncle was telling him.

He listened but he wasn't surprised. And from the house they all came running, their faces contorted, crying, even laughing. It didn't seem to matter. Perhaps he was tired. "Don't you tell them now," his uncle pleaded.

"No," he said.

Question

David Cornel DeJong

Once we had fields for our hopes, the lakes
Along our plantings full of morning glowing.
What is it that the months did, that time takes,
To find now only a space with day sowing
Its old colds, where once we harrowed so well,
Where we hoped, heads to the soil, hearing
The gulls above us, as if hearing could quell
Their white petulance on all our fearing?

What have the years done that we never saw
The seeping away of dreams amid our toiling,
Never the ending, till at last the air was raw
With crows, with grackles, and harvest spoiling
Upon the stalks; when we bent no more, and fear
With youth had gone like a thrush and swallow
Beyond all sight, and crows came very near
To scratch the earth already still and fallow?

The hours have dropped unto snow, the sky
At last lies tight upon all wonder,
That nothing may breathe, nothing ask why
It was the gulls we dared not hear (not thunder
Or bellowing beasts on a neighboring hill)
Only the white birds high, and their silver falling
Never for the eyes, only for ears, so long until
All earth was filled with fear and naked calling.

In Memoriam

David Cornel DeJong

Here, where the grass is lusher than. . . .
Here, where the winds bleach, and the sun. . . .
Here lies my son. . . . Over him silence
And noise go on as over anything once man
But now just bone. The days go on.

Ask me in whatever voice you may. . . .
I know no answer, none was given me
When yearning meant food, when words paraded
With banners of truth, none when faith lay
At last on its utmost bed and ceased to be.

I fed him patience, peace. I wrapped
All his breathing in hope; and what I knew
Of love I planted where his mind mellowed
And could taste. . . . But there was no drum I tapped
For war. And evil came, and evil grew.

Was he unarmed? . . . But, he stood straight,
Lifting his neck, holding very high
His head, squaring his strength. Alone—he stumbled
And lay in blood and flies and groans. No great
Angel was there to slake his awful cry.

Why chisel lecture, praise or even name
Here where he is again alone? Save breath
And motion for a gaudier game; why gamble
Remorse away at this stand, at this game
Of which the only pay-off is death?

Autumn

William Styron

WEATHERBY stood at the edge of the grassy bank which sloped down from the school to the river. The October breeze fanned the wisps of gray hair on his head. He was a short little man with a round paunch, like an unripe melon, which no one could deny, of course, to a man of his years. At one time, when he was young, his waist had been as straight and hard as a cedar plank; but, after all, one does grow old. His eyes, though, even after years of grading English themes, were as strong as any man of fifty-eight could claim, and as he stood there he could pick out the tiniest houses across the river.

Weatherby always liked these early morning walks, and this one was especially pleasing. Unless it was raining, he would arise at six, an hour before the colored boy rang the bell to wake up the boys. Then he would take a quick shower in the bathroom, which he shared with the upper-form boys. Afterwards he would dress, sometimes in the gray tweed suit which the headmaster's wife had said was so becoming to him, and walk briskly down the stairs and out onto the campus. This walk was a daily ritual with him, and his path would invariably follow through the woods which stretched eastward down the river. Now and then, near some venerable oak or at a quiet little spot beside the lake, cool and shadowy in the dawn, he would hold reverent communion with himself. During moments like these, when he felt especially humble in the glow of God's morning, he would almost imagine himself in Wordsworth's shoes, and he would try to imagine what *he* would say at such a time. Then he would recite out loud, thrilling somewhat to the sound of his slow, measured voice, lines from Wordsworth or Matthew Arnold, both of whom, like himself, were disciples of Nature.

At the end of his walk he stood for a while and gazed at the river, the river which in its blue calmness never ceased to be a source of beauty for him. He would put all of that in his book, he thought. That would add a depth, a resonance, to the lyrical passages. "The great Rappahannock, the American Oxus, gulching the clay-ribbed land with its slow blue course, flowing silently, ever onward and downward to the sea." His heart now gave a sudden jump as he thought of the great bottomless well of emotion within him, the *bigness* of it all, and with that he recited aloud, a little choked, the entire middle part of *Tintern Abbey.*

He heard Richard, the colored boy, whistling as he came across the yard to wake up the boys.

"Good morning, Richard," he said, full of vigor. "Nice day, eh?"

Richard smiled, tugging on the rope of the heavy bell.

"Mawnin', suh! Yassuh!"

Weatherby rubbed his hands briskly, staring at the sky with his neck craned in mock concentration.

"Ah-h, let's see, Thursday morning, ah-h, could it be that we have, ah-h . . . scrambled eggs today?"

Richard laughed a throaty Negro laugh.

"Yas-*suh!* You always guesses it right!"

As he walked toward the dormitory he thought a bit unpleasantly about the watery scrambled eggs, which usually put him in an uncomfortable mood for breakfast. But strangely enough the food at St. Stephen's was much better than at the other schools. Littlefields, for instance, which was so heavily endowed that it could have afforded roast pheasant every day. Dear God, how many meals had he eaten at those schools? First there was Benton, ten years mastership there, just after he graduated, then Beaumont, then Weldon, Crendall, St. Mark's (he would have been department head if that infernal Westcott hadn't swaggered his way into the Board's attention), Compton, then that miserable year at Littlefields, and now here. Perhaps now he was settled for good.

Weatherby could smell the warm fragrance of coffee and toast coming from the dining room in the basement. Above him, from the second floor, came the sound of boys' voices and splashing water. Mrs. Pettiway, the hostess, passed him on the walk. She was a pleasant, middle-aged woman with a calm, quiet manner.

"Good morning, Mr. Weatherby," she said. "Enjoy your walk this morning?"

"Ah-h yes, Mrs. Pettiway," he beamed, "a gorgeous morning. Why, I walked almost half the way to Urbanna, basking in this *most* radiant sunshine; and do you know, I almost completely forgot to come back!"

She smiled, and they talked about the weather as they walked down into the dining room. He liked her very much. She was a widow and had been at St. Stephen's for eight years, ever since Mr. Jones had become headmaster. She had a charming apartment over the infirmary, and now and then she invited him up for coffee and to listen to Delius and Beethoven on her phonograph. Weatherby was especially fond of the *Pastoral Symphony,* and they played it nearly every Sunday night.

In the dining room he greeted the four other masters with a brisk and hearty "good-morning," reserving, of course, a more dignified greeting for Mr. Jones, who stood with his wife and daughter at the big round table in the middle of the room. As Weatherby passed him, the headmaster unbent slightly from the waist, made a little wry but agreeable smile, and murmured, "Good morning, sir." He was only about forty-eight, at least nine or ten years younger than Weatherby, a tall, thin man with gray, steely hair; gray, piercing eyes; and a lean, stolid, gray face. Indeed, thought Weatherby, everything about the man, even down to his suit and woolen socks, was gray. This grayness gave an air of coldness and impenetrability to the man, something that made him impersonally cordial, but rather unapproachable.

The buzzer sounded, and the boys stumbled noisily down the creaking stairs and into the dining room. There were five boys assigned to his table, and as each took his place he mumbled a respectful but sleepy "good-morning" to the master, which Weatherby acknowledged with a reserved nod of his head and a small trace of a smile.

After Mr. Jones had asked the blessing and Weatherby had begun ladling the smoking oatmeal into the white bowls, he noticed an empty seat at the table. He looked around him.

"Where is Calloway?" he asked.

There was no answer. The two upper-form boys, Randolph and Trimble, stared intently at their plates.

"I asked you," he repeated, "where Calloway is."

Randolph looked up at him with a strained face.

"I—I, well—"

"Go on, boy. Where is he?"

"He's sleeping, sir." The boy stared nervously back at his plate.

"Sleeping, eh? Well, you run up and tell him to get down here right away, hear? Immediately!"

Weatherby nearly choked in indignation. This was not the first time that this Calloway had caused him trouble. Imagine the little upstart sleeping through breakfast! He had given the boy fair warning the time he caught him out of his bunk at night, and now such an act of complete disregard for authority warranted an immediate report to Mr. Jones. It was enough to drive a man mad, playing nurse to such a brood of spoiled youngsters. Of course, not all of them were like Calloway; some were splendid, quiet boys, not too obviously impressed with their self-importance, but Calloway had now grown entirely out of hand. He was sixteen, an above-average student—excelled in composition—but ever since he had arrived he had borne some sort of hidden resentment against Weatherby. Perhaps it was because he had scolded the boy sharply that first night when he had caught him sneaking down the hall. At any rate, Weatherby had tried to be nice to the boy (that is, as nice as the bounds of convention between master and student could permit), but there was always a latent feeling of antagonism on Calloway's part that even at times bordered on the insolent.

In the first place, Weatherby knew that he did not have that certain knack of handling boys. He did not have a "way" with them, that gentle, soothing, soft persuasion and indomitable heartiness which turned schoolmasters from pedagogues into doddering, plum-ripe old fools. Although he himself was not too strict a disciplinarian, he rested assured in the fact that he would never approach that idealized, picturesque state he had seen so often, that of a master, bristling with tireless energy, waddling about the campus and quoting platitudes to his charges with the amiable nonchalance of Falstaff. In the second place, Weatherby was fundamentally a scholar. He would never, no, never, let himself fall into the degenerate role of certain masters he had known who complacently smiled down at their boys with dew-rimmed eyes, declaiming from Cicero in a quavering, honeyed voice, and generally acting the part of a wise and kind old walrus. No, Weatherby had found that, although he was never too popular with his students, he would always be essentially the scholar, dispensing knowledge with a firm and just hand, completely free from any drooling, extra-curricular sophistry . . . all of which made him very, very happy.

Weatherby mused reflectively over his oatmeal, listening idly to the murmured breakfast conversation. His eyes wandered over to Ridley's table. The boys at the table were laughing uproariously, probably at one of Ridley's jokes. He was a tall, handsome young man with a lean, athletic body and a tanned face. He coached football and taught biology and lower-form arithmetic. Weatherby noticed that the boys adored him. On the football field Ridley swore at them with a soft, Deep-South enunciation, which seemed to endear him that much more to the boys. Weatherby thought it rather disgusting. As he took his walk through the fields in the afternoon, or stood above the windswept playing field, he often could hear the young man's voice clear and frosty in the autumn air:

"God damn it, McLeod, over tackle, over tackle!"

Yes, it *was* disgusting!

Randolph and Calloway came into the dining room, Calloway sneaking in through the side door so as to be unnoticed by Mr. Jones.

The infernal cheek of the little rascal!

As Calloway took his place, Weatherby spoke to him.

"Well, sir," he demanded, "what does this mean? What do you mean by being late to breakfast?"

The boy gave a little grimace, somewhat suspicious of a nasty scowl.

"I—I, well, I was sleepy, sir."

"Here, here," he spluttered, "do you think that's any excuse? Do you? Do you?"

The boy muttered something beneath his breath. Probably an oath, Weatherby thought.

"What's that you said?"

The smaller boys at the table were nudging each other in delight.

"I said, sir, that I studied late last night, and I was sleepy."

"It makes no difference whether you were studying or not—" he was almost shouting—"you must, *must* be punctual!" Then, in a lower voice, with a sigh of finality, he said: "It shall be my duty to report the matter to Mr. Jones." The breakfast proceeded in silence.

Weatherby held English class at nine o'clock. It was the upper-form class in literature, and he had scheduled a test for the day. He bustled into the class with the papers under his arm.

"Well, well," he said, erasing the board in broad, vigorous strokes, "a little examination today, eh, gentlemen?"

The boys groaned in pained resignation.

"Come, come, gentlemen," he chuckled, "it's not as bad as all that!"

As he passed out the papers, he noticed that all of them, except Tidewell, were seething at his affected good humor. Calloway glared at him, then turned away. Tidewell, on the other hand, faithful, studious, brilliant Tidewell, smiled at him with a broad, gleaming mouthful of orthodontic braces.

"Thank you, sir," he said.

As he turned, someone hit the back of Tidewell's head with a piece of chalk.

Now they were all at work, bent over their desks. For a minute he watched them closely. He must keep a lookout for wandering eyes. The windows were open, and a gentle breeze, warmed by the bright October sun, fanned his face. He became drowsy, and looked out of the window. An immense green fly droned lazily above the window sill and settled on the screen next to him. His gaze traveled from the fly out onto the green campus, past the two gnarled cedars and the little chapel, its stained-glass windows glistening in the sun. Beyond the chapel and the clay road the blackened meadow stretched its charred stubble to the border of the woods. Even from where he sat he could see the brown oak leaves falling and fluttering through the burnished foliage. The gaunt green pines stood out against the other trees, drenched in the red of fall. He could name the trees from the color of their leaves. A wispy wreath of blue smoke curled from the bottomlands upward to meet the lighter blue of the sky, now splotched with little puffy clouds drifting sleepily to the west.

Weatherby nearly fell asleep, but was awakened by the deep humming of the fly, which renewed its lethargic activity on the window screen. He heard the soft rustling of the papers and the steady scratching of thirteen pencils. Through the window drifted the heavy autumnal smell of burning leaves, the familiar odor that made him think of rotting stumps smoldering in the distant, loamy bottomlands.

The buzzer rang at last, and Weatherby nodded upward with a start. The boys were still working on their tests, trying to struggle through the last, impossible question.

"Come, come, gentlemen," he said; "time is up. Turn in your papers."

Calloway bit his pencil and scowled. The boys handed in their papers sullenly and trooped out of the room. Weatherby heard one of them sigh an agonized "Jesus Christ." Perhaps the test was a bit intensive, but he prided himself on stimulating the boys to effort.

After lunch Weatherby had coffee with Mr. Jones at the headmaster's table.

"Mr. Jones," he said, "I think I should inform you of some—er—misconduct on the part of Calloway."

The headmaster rapped on the table with a cigarette, arched his gray eyebrows, and leaned back in his chair.

"Frankly, sir, I think the boy is a misfit. Why, only

this morning he came to breakfast five minutes late. And he has taken a peculiar aversion to me, which at times borders on rank insolence. Now I don't want to appear overbearing, but—"

"I see, I see, Mr. Weatherby. The boy has me stumped too. Something definitely will have to be done."

Then somehow the headmaster changed the subject.

Later Weatherby went up to his room on the second floor of the dormitory. His door opened out onto the hall where the boys slept. The dormitory, with the classrooms beneath, was built in the shape of a T. Instead of rooms the boys slept in small cubicles which lined both sides of the hallway. The master's room was well situated, for from his room at night he could keep an ear cocked for any disturbance coming from the corridor. Whenever Weatherby heard the sound of stealthy creakings, he would creep softly to the door, flashlight in hand, then suddenly fling it open and trap the culprit in the beam of light. Old as he was, he could still pride himself on a certain amount of speed and agility.

He went in, seated himself at his desk, and began to mark the day's test papers. After a few papers he began to get sleepy, and, shoving the tests aside, he reached for the sheaf of manuscript beneath the desk. Thumbing through the last pages, he noted an error and corrected it in a small, neat hand. The manuscript, written at long intervals over a period of ten years, was a collection of formal essays—mostly fragmentary, since Weatherby wrote at his utmost leisure—consisting mainly of critiques, in a philosophical vein, of most of the major poems of Arnold and Wordsworth, with a word or two here and there on Sophocles and the Stoics. Although it was impossible for him to believe that he had been writing so long, he was not nearly finished. Only when he was aroused by the heat of inspiration, stimulated by some grand solemnity of Nature—an oak, or a great river—could he push himself to the agonizing torture of forming the twenty-six symbols of the alphabet into their mystic combinations. Someday his essays would be published. Someday. And he was comforted by the thought that the intolerable boredom of school-mastering could be relieved in some measure by his contact with Nature, the quietness of the sparse but unspoiled countryside, the sacred communication between himself and the earth which he held close-locked within him—but which could finally be released in a flooding glory of prose. *The Earth Is Mine: A Collection of Formal Essays on Nature,* by George Weatherby. He sighed deeply.

As he checked back over the manuscript, he heard Calloway's voice coming from below on the campus. He winced sharply and was suddenly surprised at the gesture. Now why on earth had he done that? he wondered. This situation with the boy was beginning to irritate him. Although many times before there had been boys who had given him trouble, he had never had a case quite like this. The boy must have been utterly spoiled. Weatherby had seen him when he first arrived at school at the beginning of the term, with his father, a rich, hearty-looking businessman from Richmond. The father, so it was said, was a staunch and loyal churchman and had contributed not a little in support of the school. Perhaps that was the reason Mr. Jones was so hesitant in disciplining the boy with any degree of strictness.

But there was no doubting it: the boy disliked him fiercely. He could see the look behind Calloway's sullen eyes. The boy was a leader; he got along well with the others, but the master was quick to notice that there was an element of—well, sneakiness in him, and a rejection of authority. Of course he would, like the other boys, respond readily to the mandates of that young boor, Ridley, but when Weatherby himself attempted any measure of control, there was quick and immediate repulsion. Perhaps it was because Weatherby was of the "old school" of teaching. His habit of aloofness and reserve (which, after long years, he had conceded to be the best approach, in the long run, to master-student relations) had evidently rebuffed Calloway from the beginning. All of which was extremely unfortunate, but he would certainly not discard his theory for the benefit of one recalcitrant boy. True, he had been a bit harsh with the boy that night when he caught him out of his bunk. . . .

Then suddenly a wave of indignation came over him, partly because of Calloway's loud voice beneath the window—the harsh crow-sound of a boy whose voice is changing; but he was irritated more for letting the thought of the whole matter, a completely silly, trivial thing, goad him into such a state of nervousness. He slammed down the window angrily, scattering the pages of his manuscript over the desk. Tonight, he thought, he would drive over to Urbanna for a few beers. They would do him good. He had found a place when he first came to St. Stephen's the year before where he could have a few drinks without attracting the attention of either the students or the faculty. Although he well knew that what he did with his spare time was his own business, he had thought it best to keep such activity to himself. It was harmless enough an enjoyment—a beer or two at Bristow's (dear God, he had no other occasion for recreation, except for the chats with Mrs. Pettiway on Sunday nights)—but being at a church school and all that, well, one could never tell what nasty rumors might spring up.

Weatherby worked for nearly two hours, grading themes and checking the test papers. Calloway, he noticed, had written an extraordinarily good theme on sailing. He gave him a B-plus and then went to dinner.

After dinner Weatherby walked across the campus to the garage, backed his Chevrolet around the dusty driveway, and drove the four miles to Urbanna. The shadowed, orange glow of October dusk had already fallen over the little town when he parked his car behind Bristow's Cafe. From where he stood he could see a flock of seagulls squawking noisily over the marshy river shore, paling now in the twilight. He went in and sat down in one of the booths near the back, where he could look out of the window toward the river.

The boy behind the counter brought him a beer, and he began to drink. It tasted good. Almost immediately he started to feel better. The feeling of depression which had come over him during the afternoon fell off quickly after

two beers, but soon the slight sense of exhilaration wore into a sort of pleasant meditation. He gazed out of the window toward the darkening river, lying calm and wide, like a misty shadow, in the last fading gold of the sun. Far over on the shore, dotted with tiny white farmhouses, a pale rind of moon was rising behind a hazy pall of autumnal smoke. As he gazed at the river, once more he was impressed with its flowing, somnolent beauty, its weary, everlasting strength, running out like a man's life to the sea.

Weatherby turned away from the window and ordered another beer. This was his third bottle. He knew that he shouldn't drink too much, but he ordered another anyway. The record player was playing a Western song, sung by a man with a guitar and a sad voice.

I've drifted all alone, no one to call my own;
Don't leave me now to face the lonely years. . . .

For some reason the song, the sad, vibrant, far-away sound of the guitar affected him deeply. It made him think of old, forgotten time, of autumn twilight, of hearing the song in some imaginary place in the West, of the lonely guitar echoing back from the bare and vacant hills. It was a music strange and foreign to him, a lover of Beethoven, but there was something about it, a forlorn sadness that was inescapable. It was a melody of lost love, and barren years; and the mournful wail of the distant guitar summoned thoughts, bell-like, from the past.

You said we'd never part; don't leave and break my heart.
I love you, dear; don't let your sweet love die. . . .

There was a voice which came like a shaft of sunlight from his childhood:

"George! George Weatherby!"

Then there was the dreamlike awakening, the cool October breeze from beneath the window crack, and the morning light on his pillow. And his mother's voice again:

"George! Wake up, George!"

And there were other voices that came to him suddenly, mistily: the voices of children calling to him from beneath the sycamores, dropping like bird-notes from the past.

"Georgie is a scairty-cat . . . a scairty-cat . . . a scairty-cat. . . ."

Then the voices grew more insistent and loud, a whole multitude of voices that marched through his mind, whispering and clamoring for attention. They came and faded and came again, like the tinkling of spinet music in a drowsy flow of dreams. As he heard them and the sound of the distant guitar, Weatherby knew that he was like any other man who grew old, who sat in little cafes at twilight listening to faraway music, and who mused in a hazy, sorrowful dream over the fallen years.

I've drifted all alone, no one to call my own. . . .

He sat for a time listening to the music and drinking beer. Then, after paying his bill, he walked, a bit unsteadily, out to his car and drove back to school. It was not a long trip, but he took his time going by the river road. When he got to school it was almost bedtime. As he climbed the stairs, he noticed that one of the other masters had turned the light off in the hall. Twice he stumbled going up the steps. That beer, he thought, had certainly taken its toll of his perceptual faculties. Never before had he allowed it to affect him so.

He was very sleepy. The beer had made his mind hazy and thick. Without even brushing his teeth—he was usually meticulous about his toilet—he turned out the light on his desk and got into bed. Before he had turned over beneath the covers more than twice, he began to hear soft noises in the corridor. There was nothing more than the creaking of a loose board, the sound of stifled laughter, which crept half-heard through the opaque shadow in his mind. Then, when he was about to drowse off, he was abruptly wakened by a tumbling, crashing sound at the far end of the hall, and the sound of hoarse, choked laughter which was suspiciously like Calloway's. Weatherby climbed out of bed, threw on his bathrobe, and fumbled in the dark for his flashlight. As he stood erect, the room lurched in the pale glow of the moon from the window. The commotion was louder now, and he could plainly hear the sound of boys' voices. He flung open the door and flashed the light down the hall. As he did, he caught sight of pajama-clad figures scurrying into their cubicles. Walking down the hall, he half-stumbled against the radiators and heard excited, whispered warnings coming from the direction of Calloway's bunk. He would put a stop to that! He flashed his light into the cubicle. Inside, on the bed, Calloway and Marks sat, the remnants of a cake between them. They stared back at the light without blinking.

"What is the meaning of this?" His voice was blurred, and he could hear himself shouting.

There was no answer from either of the boys. They gazed straight at him, and Weatherby thought he could detect a trace of a smile on Calloway's lips. His head was pounding, and the boys' faces wavered in a fog before his eyes. It was all very strange, the silence and Calloway's unwavering gaze. To cover his nervousness he played the light around in the corner of the cubicle. Then in a voice which was stern, but which he thought was more tempered, he said:

"All right. Which one of you was responsible for all the noise down here?"

There was still no answer. Then suddenly, from an adjoining bunk there came words which shocked him. They were horrible, coming from the mouth of a boy; but what jolted him more was the manner in which the words were delivered:

"You drunk old bastard!"

Sneering, muffled, mocking words. And then the whole hall burst into an uproar of laughter. Weatherby was unable to say a word. He was stunned, while the laughter came back, wave on wave, through his confused mind. He spluttered feebly, trying to recover his authority and dignity.

"Who—what—who was that that said that?"

It was unbelievable, untrue, but it was happening, and through all the turmoil in his brain he could feel his self-confidence toppling. Calloway and Marks broke out into broad grins, but a certain solemnity, born out of respect for the master, caused their faces to become drawn and serious.

"You—you," he muttered, pointing a finger at Calloway, on whom he laid unaccountably all of the blame. "I—I shall feel it my duty to. . . . You report to Mr. Jones in the morning! Hear me? Hear me?"

Then he fumbled his way, almost stupefied with shame and humiliation, up the hall and into his room. As he slowly closed the door, he could still hear the boys' laughter. How had they known? Was it his breath, or had they heard him as he stumbled up the stairs? Maybe someone had seen him in Urbanna. He didn't know, but the whole thing had confused him so that he had to sit down and think. His cheeks were still flushed with anger and shame, and a quick, sharp feeling of self-repugnance came over him. Imagine, after all these years, to be unable to cope with such a situation! It was frightful. How would he face them in the morning? Should he go out now and make a stern rebuttal, let the little mongrels feel the full lash of his wrath? Or should he demand a full apology in the morning and promise to report them, and especially Calloway, to Mr. Jones?

What bothered him the most, though, was the way in which he had failed to master the situation. Of course, he had been drinking, but never before had he so lost control of himself. It was weakness, pure and simple, or merely his age . . . his age.

Then suddenly, as if blown in through the window by the smoke-laden autumn breeze, a rending pain of loneliness came over him. From the river came the sound of a distant whistle, and his years swept down upon him like fallen leaves.

A Piece of Bread

Frances Gray Patton

LIDA was afraid to cross the street where the chain gang was working, but she knew she had to. She had promised Mother to come home and bathe at five, and besides it was wrong to be afraid, and besides what could possibly hurt her. The Negro prisoners were all coupled together by heavy chains at their ankles, and a white man with a gun was watching them. She would go quietly across in a grown-up way, and nobody would even notice her. Of course, she could walk down and cross at the corner and then walk back up to her own house on the other side. But that would be going out of her way for no real reason; Mother might see her and ask her why she was coming from the wrong direction. And she would have to say she had been afraid.

She helped Annie Byrd pick up the scraps from their paper-doll cutting, and then she said goodbye, she had to go.

"Oo-ooh, Lida!" said Annie Byrd. "Ain't you scared to cross the street with those old convicts there?" She rolled her round, china-blue eyes. "Don't you wish my papa was here with that great big old seven-passenger Pierce Arrow automobile he's gonna buy? Oh me! He would give you a ride home in it. You wouldn't be scared then. He would run it right through that chain gang, right over the sidewalk, right up in your front yard. Oh my!" Annie Byrd bounced up and down, laughing and holding her fat stomach with her hands. "Those niggers wouldn't know what to think when he came chug-chugging through 'em!"

Annie Byrd was certainly silly, thought Lida. The idea of Mr. Byrd running over those men! As for the automobile, she would believe in that when she saw it. Grandmother said automobiles were all right for New York, or even Baltimore, but that in a small Southern town they were out of place and ostentatious.

"No," said Lida, "I'm not scared."

As she walked down the brick path, she worried about having told Annie Byrd a story. She paused, with her hand on the iron gate, half a mind to go back and tell her that, yes, she really was afraid. But the courthouse clock was striking five, and Annie Byrd was so silly. And, after all, she had not quite told a story. It was not exactly a scared feeling she had—how could you be scared when there was nothing to be scared of?—it was more a kind of nervousness about making herself conspicuous.

The afternoon was hot and still. After the shade of the Byrds' vine-screened porch, the light hurt her eyes; it shimmered like the wavy lines on a water-silk hair ribbon. The air smelled of dust, and the prisoners' hot, wet bodies, and the heavy sweetness of magnolia trees in flower. It was very quiet. Even the English sparrows in the magnolias were silent. There was no sound except the scrape of shovels, the clank of chains. Most colored people sang when they worked, thought Lida. Capitola did in the kitchen, and so did the field hands out at the farm. Maybe these men were not allowed to sing. Maybe the man with the gun would shoot them if they did. Or maybe the chains made them so tired they didn't feel like singing.

Thinking about the chains made her own legs feel light and free. She wanted to skip, to leap, just because she could. But she knew that would be unkind, like staring at a cripple or imitating somebody who stuttered. She looked across at her house—white, dignified, with the big brass knocker on its bottle-green door, and its blinds still closed against the sun. Very sedately Lida stepped into the street.

But as she did, a man spoke to her.

"Little Missy," he said, "could you git me a morsel of dry bread?"

He was a grotesquely built Negro. His legs were so short that he stood not much taller than Lida; but his trunk and shoulders were powerful, and the horizontal stripes of his convict clothes made them appear enormous. His head was perfectly round and bald. It sat between his huge shoulders like a small black cannon ball. His yellow eyes, anxious, desperate, besought her like the eyes of an animal in pain. He ran the purple tip of his tongue along his cracked lips before he spoke again. His mouth scarcely moved at all as he whispered:

"Jes' a piece of cold, dry cornbread, please ma'am, Little Missy. It don't matter if it's hard and dry. Jes' a—"

"All right," Lida nodded, and fled across the street.

She was spent with terror by the time she reached her front door. She could feel the goose bumps cold along her arms. She leaned against the door-frame to get her breath before she went in. She looked at them, working in the street. The man who stopped her was not looking at her; he was busy with his shovel, scraping the dirt smooth along the curb, as if nothing had happened. But she knew he was waiting. He was waiting for her, Lida, to come back with a piece of cornbread.

She was not going back. She would die of fright if she had to look again into the miserable eyes of that nigger. (Not nigger, colored man.) Her heart was beating too fast; she might have a heart attack and drop dead out there in the middle of the chain gang. And suppose the guard should speak to her. Lida saw him sitting on the stone carriage block with his gun across his knees. The back of his neck was red. She saw him stretch and spit. Suppose he should raise his gun and holler at her. Suppose he should say: "What are you doing here, little girl?" She was not going back.

But, then, she had to, didn't she? She looked at the sky.

"I can't," she whispered, almost defiantly; "I'm too little."

She went into the house. She closed the door behind her very gently, so as not to disturb Mother and Grandmother, who were still lying down. She took off her shoes and tiptoed up the stairs; she slid her feet softly over the straw matting in the upstairs hall. Grandmother was asleep; Lida could hear her delicate, lacy snoring. But Mother called to her in a low voice.

"Lida," said Mother, "you're a good girl. You came home just when I told you to."

Lida stopped at Mother's open door. Mother was lying on her big bed under a canopy of blue mosquito netting. In her white cambric nightgown, with her small, pink, bare feet, she had the girlish look that surprised Lida every time she saw her resting on a summer afternoon.

"You look tired, though, Lida. Have you and Annie Bryd been running in the hot sun?"

"No, ma'am," said Lida. "Mrs. Byrd made us play on the piazza."

Capitola appeared in the hallway with her arms full of clean towels. She was a tall, majestic woman. Her skin was the color of a roasted coffee bean. She had a proud, Jewish nose; she looked sternly down it at Lida.

"Why didn't you call me, Lida?" she asked. "That chain gang in the road! I'd have brought you home. You had no call to cross the road by yourself betwixt them wild men."

"Nonsense, Capitola," said Mother. "Don't frighten the child. What could possibly hurt her?"

Capitola went on to the linen closet without a word. She walked like an Egyptian queen, thought Lida. There was a picture of one in her Sunday School leaflet. Capitola wore a charm bracelet around her ankle. It tinkled as she walked.

"The men were perfectly respectful to you, weren't they, Lida?"

"Oh, yes, ma'am," said Lida. "They were perfectly respectful."

Lida lingered in the doorway. She wanted to tell Mother about the man who had asked for the bread. Only, she thought, Mother might make her take it to him. Mother might get up and fix a plate with ham and cold sweet potatoes and cornbread, and make her march right over there with it. With everybody looking on—the other prisoners, and Annie Byrd, and everybody—and the guard saying, "What are you doing here, little girl?" Especially if Mother guessed she was afraid.

That was how grown people were. If they saw you were afraid to go somewhere, they made you go. Mother and Grandmother had made her take the water, that time, to the old dog who was dying. Lida had loved the old dog. She had wanted to run away from his moaning and from his pitiful eyes. But they had said: "No, Lida, you must face things." When she had brought the pan of water, the old dog had licked at her hand. Mother had said: "You will feel better now, darling, because you have been brave." But Lida had not felt better.

They were all like that, even Father. He might hold your hand and go with you. But he made you go.

Only Capitola said everybody had a right to be afraid of something. Capitola was afraid of thunder. When it stormed, she would stop work, whatever she was doing. She would not even speak. But Capitola was colored. It was natural for colored people to be afraid, because their ancestors came from the African jungles, where lions and tigers and other dangerous animals were always prowling around. It was not so for white people. Not for Lida's kind of white people. And if they knew she was afraid of the guard, they would be ashamed of her. All of them—even Capitola—they would be ashamed of her. Why, he was nothing but white trash. You weren't supposed to pay any attention at all to people like that. You just went right on and did what you knew was right; and what they said or thought didn't make any difference.

The shadow of the blue mosquito netting gave Mother's complexion a pale, faraway look. Suppose Mother should die, thought Lida. Suppose she should die, and I had kept something from her!

"Annie Byrd said her papa was going to buy a Pierce Arrow automobile!" said Lida.

"I declare!" Mother said, laughing quietly. "My soul and body, what will those Byrds think up next? Well, run take your bath, Lida. Take a good, long one, and get rested."

Lying in the bathtub, lifting the big sponge and squeezing cool water, like rain, down on her stomach, Lida relaxed and felt easier. What was there to get so upset about? The chain gang was just working in the street the way it did every year, and one of the men had asked for a piece of bread. There was nothing wrong about that. The noises from the street floated up to her, but they seemed to come from a great distance. The jangle of the chains had a peaceful sound, like that of country church bells. When I'm dressed, thought Lida, I'll take him the bread.

But once she was out of the tub, her courage began to fail her. She did not want to go back. That man frightened her. His shoulders were too big; he was like a misshapen gnome in a fairy tale. He made her feel sorry, as if she were somehow to blame for his troubles. And he must be a bad man or he wouldn't be there. But he was hungry. He was waiting for her. He thought she was going to bring him a piece of bread.

Suppose he should lick at her hand the way the old dog had.

What should she say if the guard spoke to her?

She sprinkled violet-scented talcum powder on her body. Some of it fell, like fine snow, upon the dark bathroom floor. Carefully she wiped it up with a wad of dampened toilet paper. She threw the paper into the toilet bowl, and when she pulled the chain to flush it away, the roaring of the water shut out, for a brief, happy time, the noise of th' chain gang.

She dressed slowly, carefully. She put on lace-edged drawers that buttoned on to a "body-waist" with feather-stitching around the armholes. She buttoned a short, full petticoat over the drawers. She put on a white dress. She ran a pink ribbon through the beading at the waist; it took her a long time to do that. She stood in front of the looking glass and combed her hair. She parted it first on the right side, and then in the middle, and then on the left side.

Outside, the sound of the dragging chains grew louder. She ran to the window. The men were moving on. She crouched there, peering out between the slats of the blinds, watching them go. They moved down the street slowly on their heavy, shackled feet. After a while they were gone.

When Father came home, he said Lida looked mighty pretty; he liked to see a little girl in a white dress. Grandmother said there was nothing prettier than a clean face. (The man on the chain gang hadn't had a clean face.) Mother said for Lida to come and help put supper on the table.

"Capitola had a call right in the middle of fixing supper," said Mother. "Really, her professional duties are a trial to the flesh."

Father laughed and Grandmother sighed. Capitola was a midwife. Mother had told her about it ages ago when she was only eight. Grandmother had wondered if Lida was old enough to understand, but Mother had said Lida ought to know about those things. Capitola, Mother said, was good at helping babies to be born. So they had to let her off now and then, even when it was inconvenient, because it wasn't fair to trust little colored babies' lives to someone who might not know the best way, when their Capitola was so clean and good. After all, the Good Lord made the colored babies, too.

They had Sally Lunn and creamed chicken and cold, sliced tomatoes for supper. Grandmother ate her tomatoes in the old-fashioned way, with sugar and vinegar. Lida wondered idly how she could. Lida picked at her food. What would they think of me, she wondered, if they knew I was afraid to take a hungry man a piece of bread?

Capitola came back in time to serve dessert. When she brought in the sliced peaches and cream, Father said:

"How was the fishing, Cappy?"

The suggestion of a smile twitched at the corners of

Capitola's mouth, gleamed for an instant in the whites of her eyes. She had been Father's nurse when he was a little boy, and he was the only person she ever smiled at, even as much as that.

"I cotch me a fine ten-pound boy," she said.

"Capitola," said Grandmother coldly, without looking at her.

"Yes, ma'am," said Capitola. "Scuse me, ma'am."

But they all knew it was Father who had been rebuked.

Nobody liked Grandmother's displeasure, because it was always just. Her sight was failing, and she had very little to do but think about being good. She would often sit for hours with her Prayer Book open upon her lap. She would examine a page for a while through her reading glass, and then she would gaze quietly into space. If you asked her, she could always tell you the exact difference between what was right and what was wrong. Imagine any chain gang guard, thought Lida, asking Grandmother what she was doing there!

"You aren't eating, honey," said Father.

Mother said, "I'm afraid Lida and Annie Byrd ran around in the hot sun."

"No, ma'am," said Lida, "we played paper-dolls on the piazza." She looked at Mother and Father. Their faces were full of loving concern. She had to tell them. "A man spoke to me when I crossed the street," she said.

"What!" cried Mother. "Oh, Lida, you didn't tell me!"

"He wanted a little piece of dry bread."

"One of the convicts workin' on the road," said Capitola. "I told Lida she had no call to cross by herself."

"Go 'long, Cappy," said Father. "What could possibly hurt her?"

"I think he was hungry," said Lida.

"I shouldn't wonder," said Father. "You know," he went on, turning to Mother and Grandmother, "the Grand Jury ought to investigate these road camps. I've an idea that the graft that goes on there is appalling. You hear too many stories of half-starved convicts."

"I didn't get him the bread," said Lida.

"The guards are apt to be the very scum of the earth," said Father.

"Who else would have the job?" said Mother.

"But you can't imagine the sort of men they are," said Father.

"I didn't get him the bread," said Lida.

Father looked at her, kindly, seriously. He turned his whole attention upon her.

"You didn't?" he said. "Why didn't you, honey?"

Lida ran the tip of her tongue along her lips the way the man had. It was hard to make the words come, but she was going to tell him. Father had asked her, and she was going to tell him all about it. Even about being afraid of the guard.

Grandmother lifted her beautiful, misty eyes and looked at Father.

"The child was right," said Grandmother. "Who is she, a little girl ten years old, to interfere in the discipline of Negro criminals? It would have been unsuitable." She smiled at Lida. "Render unto Caesar the things that are Caesar's," she said.

"Oh, of course," said Father hastily. "I wasn't criticizing Lida. Lida did right."

"Lida is a good girl," murmured Mother. "She came home precisely on time."

"She ought to call me when the road's full of wild men," said Capitola.

"That will do, Capitola," said Grandmother. "Life is full of unpleasant experiences, Lida. We will not speak of this one again. Eat your peaches."

Obediently, Lida took her spoon and stirred the peaches around in the saucer of thick cream. Capitola walked softly, haughtily to the kitchen, her chain of charms rattling as she walked. Mother laughed, and began to talk about Mr. Byrd's proposed motor car.

They sat together there, lingering over their peaches in the deepening twilight. They did not turn on the light because it would attract moths, and because it would be a waste of electricity, and because the dimness gave the room an illusion of coolness. A breeze came in through the curtainless window, bringing with it the odor of magnolia blossoms. It was a different odor now without the sun to draw out its heaviness. It smelled cool and dry, like the inside of a little wooden matchbox.

"Feel the breeze?" said Father.

Lida was scarcely aware of the talk that flowed about her, monotonous and familiar. Nobody noticed that Lida had laid down her spoon and was staring out of the open window. She sat, withdrawn into a dreamlike loneliness, gazing through the window at the street.

It was a different street, she felt, from the one she had crossed in the hot, late afternoon. It was changed, like the smell of the magnolias. It was still and empty. It was empty of everything but the green, leafy gloom of trees that gave it a beauty at once friendly and magical. Soon the evening would take away the color of the leaves, and in the gray dusk the arc lamps would come on at the street corners. They would not come on all at one time, but—beginning way down at the courthouse corner—they would twinkle up the street, one after one, the way the first few stars crop out in the sky. Then, suddenly, as if the lighting of the last corner lamp were a signal, night would fall. The day would be closed forever.

A colony of English sparrows, roosting in one of the trees, began a coarse, twittering quarrel. They jostled one another and rustled the stiff magnolia leaves. That faint, harsh sound grated along Lida's nerves like the echo of a vague anxiety. Somehow, the shadows in the street had lost their quality of peace and kindliness. Among them someone was waiting for her. He was still waiting.

And out of the gathering darkness one shadow, darker than the rest, lengthened, and invaded the innermost recesses of her mind. It brooded there, black and shapeless, tingeing all her thoughts with the somber hue of its trouble.

"To the Wilderness Dead"

Mary Gus Rodgers

IT WAS a beautiful fall day, crisp and clear, with a sky like a great blue flag. "Terrific day for football," Chet murmured as they walked toward the car, their footsteps rustling among the dried leaves that covered the path. And for a moment, just a moment while she was so conscious of the sunlight and the smell of dusty leaves in the air, she thought that they were really walking hand in hand toward the football stadium as they had done so many times before. Pretty soon they would be close enough to hear the thump of the band, and they would push through the crowd at the gates, and Chet would buy a couple of warm coca-colas before they settled down on the hard bench and watched the cheer leaders waving their megaphones at friends in the grandstand.

Chet opened the car door. "Hop in, chum," he said. "Feel in the mood for some pioneer stuff? I thought maybe we could stop by old Fort Harrod while we're here. Never can tell when we'll be back this way."

That's absolutely right, she thought. You never can tell when we'll be back this way. And there'll be no use in my coming back alone. Nothing will be there because you are not. Aloud, she said, "Fine idea." She started to ask if they had enough time and then changed her mind. "How did you like Beaumont Inn, darling?"

"Great old place. The way it looked, I was expecting Scarlett O'Hara to come down the steps any minute."

She handed him the cigarette he was looking for. "If she had," she said, "you wouldn't have seen her. You had your face buried in your plate the whole time."

Smiling at her, he said, "Well, maybe so. But I won't have a chance at food like that for quite a spell. I hear the Army doesn't serve much country ham. Not the real stuff anyway."

"No, I guess they don't. And they don't go in for spoon bread, either." He had started the car while she was talking, and it began to move slowly down the curving driveway. She turned around in the seat and looked out the back window. "Isn't it lovely, Chet? Isn't is a lovely old house?" He's right about Scarlett O'Hara, she thought. It had everything she connected with old Southern homes—long windows and high ceilings with dark woodwork and the sound of screen doors slamming and someone singing in the kitchen. She turned around again, toward Chet. He reached for her hand.

"We sure enough had a good time this afternoon," he said.

"Is that unusual, Chester K.?"

Suddenly his expression was very remote. He's remembering things, she realized. And you only remember best when the end is coming. "Yeah," he said. "We sure have." He rubbed his hand against hers a moment and then he finished, "I wish—I wish we'd known just how good a time we were having."

They both looked away at the same time. They were not used to talking like that, and it was a little embarrassing. She was very elaborate about lighting a cigarette for herself, and he paid a lot of attention to the job of parking in front of the fort. She waited while he got out of the car and came around to open the door for her; there was something very touching about his starting to do little things like that again. "Here we are, baby," he said. "Right where Dan'l Boone kilt that bar." He put his arm around her shoulder, and they walked toward the stockade. At the entrance, where Chet paid for admission tickets, there was a display of amazingly useless things for sale—squares of sateen with a stenciled picture of the fort, little wooden jugs, manufactured arrow heads, a framed copy of "My Old Kentucky Home."

Chet picked up the little wooden jug; when he pulled out the stopper they saw that from it a kernel of corn dangled on a string. "See, honey?" Chet said. "Corn—corn whiskey. Get it?" He bounced the little jug up and down. "God, they must have sat up nights, thinking up that idea." He smiled and she always loved his smile. His full lower lip gave his face a slightly sullen look in repose, but when he smiled the change in his expression was always startlingly sweet.

"Let's buy the little jug," she said. For a souvenir, she thought, and yet souvenirs are no good either. You can't paste laughter and a gay mood into a scrapbook.

Chet handed the little wooden scrap to her. "I know why you want it, Mrs. Astor. To prove that there is some damn thing we haven't drunk out of."

"We have drunk out of practically everything in our time, that's the truth," she said. Coca-cola in paper cups—that was picnics in the spring. And a crowded table, fraternity songs, a tent of smoke, and beer foam sliding down the sides of glasses—that was any Saturday night at the College Inn. Scotch and soda, neatly mixed by a waiter, was after the big formal dances. She remembered when they had had champagne, after the last college dance they knew they could go to together. They went to the Ivy Room at the Belmaison, and Chet had on his tails. She remembered how handsome he looked and what a glitteringly good time they had. He's such a *damn* good-looking boy, she thought. He's Young America, he's Jack Armstrong, the All-American boy. You only had to look at him to know that he had nice parents and enjoyed himself and had no particular worries, except maybe passing a few courses and worrying about who was going to win a football game.

She looked at him, standing carelessly with his hands in

his pockets, his eyes half-closed against the sun. And like a cold wind blowing through her mind was the knowledge that he was going to die. There are many ways of dying, she thought. And when they kill the person you were when you went away—well, that's as much dying as any other way. She remembered pictures she had seen in newsreels and magazines; pilots running through a cold mist that must have been the dawn toward their planes, soldiers sprawled in the grotesque postures of exhaustion, asleep on the beaches of Guadalcanal.

"It goes faster than sound, doesn't it?" she said aloud. "This plane that you fly."

Chet looked surprised for a moment and then he grinned. "Mind like a jackrabbit," he murmured. And then he said, "Thunderbolt? It only goes that fast in a dive."

"Oh," she said. "Well. That makes a lot of difference." They were walking through the fort now, and she looked at the bare log rooms with the spinning wheels and iron pots and cradles and tried to think of something to say about them. Chet picked up a broom made out of corn husks.

"Look at this, will you?" he said. "Imagine trying to sweep with this contraption. They must have had it pretty tough in those days, the women." He winked at her. "In fact, one comes to the conclusion that the girls of today aren't worth the powder that it would take—"

"We do pretty well," she interrupted. "We do pretty *damn* well." She looked around the room. You think you had it so hard, she said silently to the woman who might have lived there. Well, you can have the vacuum sweepers and the refrigerators and all the air-conditioning if you'll take the Thunderbolts, too. She was staring so steadily at the corn-husk broom that she was surprised to feel Chet behind her and see his wide brown hands on her wrists.

"Know something, Miss Stuart?" he whispered, his mouth against her ear. "I love you, Miss Stuart. And know something else? I'm going to kiss you, Miss Stuart. Right here in front of God and the ghost of Nancy Hanks."

After that, they hurried through the other buildings of the fort. As Chet said, once you've seen one pioneer room complete with spinning wheel and cradle, you've seen them all. And as Chet knew but did not say, they didn't have much time left. When they came out, she suddenly released his hand and said, "You go on and get the car. I want to see if I've missed anything." She stood and watched him running down the flight of stone steps that led to the parking lot and wished again that he hadn't had to wear his uniform. It looks tight on him, she thought. I know it fits right, but it looks tight, somehow or other.

"It's the old pioneer graveyard you haven't seen," the man at the entrance said. "It's over there on your left."

The graveyard itself was nothing but an untidy plot of grass, lumpy, with small wooden crosses and crumbling pieces of stone. But before it was a large slab of marble that shone in the late afternoon sunlight. Standing before it, feeling the wind push at her hair, she read the inscription. "TO THE WILDERNESS DEAD . . . THOSE UNBURIED, UNCOFFINED, AND UNKNOWN . . . THIS CENOTAPH ERECTED BY A NOT FORGETFUL COMMONWEALTH." She stood very straight and suddenly she spoke aloud and her voice was stern.

"Don't forget us, either," she said. And then she turned and ran down the steps to where Chet was waiting before the car.

The Cantata

Frances Wright

IT SEEMS a long time ago. It has not been so long, really, but the years have made a difference. I remember because it was a discovery and an awakening.

We lived in an apartment. I mainly remember that to enter the living room you stumbled down steps. It was a great shock to visitors, the steps lurking there, and they usually looked up in hurt surprise that you had not warned them. But aside from our traps for the unwary, there is left to remember only the warmth achieved by the over-diligent janitor and the soundlessness of footsteps in the deep rugs.

We had neighbors named Langarosse, and they were, from the first, objects of great speculation. They were strange, dark people who did not have welcoming looks on their faces. He played incessantly on a grand piano, the most impressive of their possessions. We inspected their things as they moved in, and then we found the first evidences of their incredible extravagances and their incredible poverties: a great plain bed with broken springs, a fragile white marble bust, which they cautioned must be handled with care. To us, busts were things passed on to you by relatives who didn't want them, and you kept them until you were able to find someone else not in a position to refuse the gift. We did not understand these people; of that there could be no doubt.

"Perhaps they will be cultural," said my mother. Being cultured, to her, covered a multitude of sins.

And Father, in general, disapproved of changes.

"Damned nuisance. What happened to the Bradys? Perfectly satisfactory, the Bradys." Father had been a friend of Mr. Brady's. They were both inveterate putterers-around-the-house and would spend hours happily immersed in the whys and wherefores of an ailing light switch. Father did not think Mr. Langarosse showed signs of such promise. For Father is a self-styled "rugged engineer"—the two words were inseparable with him, and after he learned of the man's peculiar addiction to music, he almost shuddered with visible disgust on passing him. Unfortunately this was happening frequently. They blundered into each other in the dark corridors. Each would back away, muttering under his breath, and Father was infuriated because the man would utter great mouthfuls of indistinguishable sound in another language. Looking back, I think that Mr. Langarosse was a very wise man and that it was better so.

It was Mother's idea that we call on them.

"After all," she said, "we are neighbors."

Being confronted with this irrefutable fact, the rest of the family yielded. I was appalled and fascinated at the thought of such a visit. I had had several glimpses of Mr. Langarosse, and I must have given somewhat the effect of a bird charmed by a snake. I followed him to his rooms usually, and, at the door, he would turn and say, "Shoo!" very much as he would to an annoying little dog. I promptly obeyed.

Mrs. Langarosse, her lavish form enveloped in a flowered apron, ushered us in. The bust was in a place of honor among the shabby furniture. The sagging chairs and the couch, like the broken-springed bed, gave the impression of having been bounded on, assailed, and generally subjected to unkind treatment. We were presented to Mr. Langarosse, then sat down gingerly.

"What do you do, Mr. Langarosse?" Father has a habit of starting acquaintances by eliciting such information.

"Do?" Mr. Langarosse said blankly. Father obviously did not think this an intelligent response.

"You know—work at?"

"Oh," Mr. Langarosse beamed and nodded his bald head fringed with black curls. "Now it is a cantata."

Mother came to the rescue.

"How—nice."

Mr. Langarosse began again. "As the saying goes—a little wine for the stomach's sake. Wine for our guests, Maria."

Maria heaved herself up from where she sat and, breathing hard, set out for the kitchen.

When she came back—

"Very fine wine," he said lovingly. "It has come a long way, this wine. Not so, little one?" He spoke to Maria. Father looked at her two-hundred pounds.

"Yes—Beau Sejour."

"My wife has called our home fatuously, and hopefully,

you understand, by that name. She has called it the beautiful stay. Ah, you do not often find such grapes or such wine as we had—"

He handed Father and Mother the slender-stemmed glasses. Father's criterion of a man is his drink. Scotch and soda, preferably. Pink Ladies and such concoctions he tolerated for Mother, swearing she chose them for the name only—which she did, in fact. But Father had been under a strain in the past moments, and the offer of wine was an unfortunate gesture.

On the way home Father turned to Mother.

"Maggie, do you really know what a cantata is?" he asked in a harried fashion.

"Why, it's some sort of music, dear. Yes, I'm sure it is."

He looked baffled.

I think perhaps the Langarosses talked to me because they were strangers and because they did not fear being misunderstood by a child, or, for that matter, being understood too well. I, with beautiful disregard for any limits between where I lived and where they lived, wandered in and out, quite happy at being ignored.

One day Mr. Langarosse said, "Some day I will write a tune for you—a little tune like a music box tinkle." Only it turned out to be full of odd jerks and discords.

"It isn't like me," I said defiantly. "It's like a grasshopper."

"No. It is you," he said with certainty.

"No." I was equally positive.

"Well," he said, considering, "maybe it's both. Maybe it's you and the grasshopper and the insect noises you hear at night. That's the trouble with my music. It gets out of hand."

I could understand that and was satisfied.

Mrs. Langarosse had a blue powder box with golden peacocks on it, I remember. The scent of the powder suffused in the heat so that it penetrated the whole apartment. The piano with its machine-gun fire of notes etched against the silence of the living room that always seemed half-darkened. These are the things I remember.

Then suddenly one day the Langarosses were happy, and everything was all right. Mr. Langarosse was dashing about distractedly, and Mrs. Langarosse was laughing, her flesh shaking with merriment. Even as far as our apartment the rejoicing was apparent.

Upon being questioned, I announced matter-of-factly to my family, "Their uncle has died."

There was more, of course; for when I went back, Mrs. Langarosse had covered her plump, pleasant face with her hands and was sobbing, while Mr. Langarosse comforted her.

"There, little one, it's all right now. We are going home, little cabbage."

"And it will be the same?"

"Yes. Yes. Why not? Mon Dieu, he was slow to die. He was a hardy one."

"Do you remember how they sang on the street-cars? I wonder if they still sing?"

"Surely. They will sing, I promise you."

"I have liked it here. You know that," she sniffled noisily. "But the money is so thick," she said with distaste, "and there's so little sun here."

"They are leaving," I scurried across the hall to report at home.

We had not thought the woman was beautiful. We

had not thought anything of the sort. Yet, somehow, we began to see the slow graciousness, the wide generous smile like sun lying on a field. We should probably never have known this but for the miracle of Mr. Langarosse's seeing it and knowing it. He came over, no longer able to contain himself, to tell us of their departure.

"We do not like to leave you," he said politely, but he did not sound as if he hated to leave. He sounded jubilant. "My uncle has died. He was a very strong man, but it was his heart in the end. A very thwarted man, my uncle. He was determined to make of me a soldier. In my youth, of course."

He shrugged apologetically, "Madam, I was not made for a soldier, le bon Dieu knows. Then Maria. It was not a strategic marriage. But she makes a man feel at peace with himself. You have noticed it? We have managed very well. Maria comes from a frugal people. We were cut off without a penny, as you would say."

They had inherited, as far as we could understand, a chateau in not very good repair and the acres around it. They had inherited the earth. The bust was carefully crated again. The night before they left was an occasion for celebration. Perhaps we were not the proper people with whom to celebrate, being without the gift of abandon as they knew it; but they were strangers in a strange land and we had to.

The wine was produced again. We sat around on packing cases among the black, many-labeled trunks. I do not think Father was happy at first, but he was being philosophical about it. As the evening went on he even grew convivial enough to start a rendition of "Mademoiselle from Armentières," though he was much startled at the elaborate leaps on the keyboard which Mr. Langarosse took in accompanying him. Mr. Langarosse would poise himself above a note and dive like an eagle on its prey.

Mr. Langarosse played his concerto in honor of the occasion, succeeding somehow in imitating a whole orchestra, his hands and feet and voice all furiously busy. He was a dynamic man of inexhaustible energy. I think in that moment Father began to have respect for him; for it was an achievement that Father himself was so obviously incapable of. He even went so far as to give Mr. Langarosse a few tips on the stock market. Of course this necessitated Mother's taking Mr. Langarosse aside to warn him about Father's confidences and predictions, which seemed invariably to turn out disastrously, but nevertheless Mr. Langarosse understood Father's good intentions.

They were in high spirits that night, the Langarosses. They talked of home, reminding each other:

"There are the two organs, one at each end of the church so that they echo each other. The midnight mass at Christmas there, there is nothing like it," Mr. Langarosse said.

"The vineyard slopes from a hill," Mrs. Langarosse continued, as if it were an often-repeated tale and she knew her cues well.

"I thought we should never pick those violets in the fields of St. Gervais," she said.

We came to understand that neither the violets nor the fields were real to them.

"My wife," Mr. Langarosse said affectionately, "once she has seen Sarah Bernhardt play. She was only a child, but she has the line—'We will never pick those violets'—it is—how shall I say?"— he spread out his hands—"a symbol. Maria is attached to the old things."

They urged food upon us—strong cheese, candied chestnuts, a small baked chicken. We were all very sad at parting. Even Mrs. Langarosse's voice, her low, quiet, clear voice, was regretful. She may have been middle-aged and fat, but she had a lovely voice.

"It has been a long wandering, Jean," she said when my parents had left, and looked at him with troubled eyes.

"Yes. But like the Greek warrior who kissed earth and was renewed, I turn to you, Maria."

She smiled at him. I tiptoed home very quietly.

Some one had to see them off. We could not let them go without the proper fluttering of handkerchiefs in the breeze. It was awkward, as is the way with farewells. We stood around, not quite sure what to say, everyone with fixed smiles. What was there to say? We had know them only briefly, after all.

"The place will seem empty without you," Mother said in a feeble effort.

"You're sure you've got everything?" Father asked.

"Yes, yes," they agreed distractedly.

Mr. Langarosse was visibly much moved. Father patted him on the back wordlessly. Either there was so much to say or so little, I am not sure which. We were a bunch of inadequate people standing in a railroad station.

"We will think of you," Mrs. Langarosse began.

Then the train was upon them, and they were gathering together their bags and innumerable newspaper-wrapped parcels. Mr. Langarosse was agitated, sure they would miss the train.

They stood on the platform, and we kept calling injunctions to one another now that the train overwhelmed the sound of our voices. In the last moment as they pulled away, Mr. Langarosse thrust a brown-wrapped bottle, which he had forgotten up until now, into Father's hands. Father held it with concealed repugnance.

"I say to myself, we must not forget and leave without giving you the wine," Mr. Langarosse yelled through the gaspings and stutterings of the train. He had put his arm around Mrs. Langarosse's waist, bracing her. They both were waving frantically to us. Their ugly, transfigured faces looked down on us.

Now I do not pretend to know about love, except that it is probably simple because people expect it to be very complicated. But I remember still Mr. Langarosse's arm around his wife's waist.

Father said savagely, "Well, we're rid of that infernal playing."

Then he did a thing odd for him. I had not seen him do such a thing for a long time. He reached for Mother's hand and held it tightly.

Confederate

George Zabriskie

Beneath the Carolina clay the immemorial thunder
Of guns is stilled, and the drums shall call
To him no longer. The blood's rebellion drained
Into the soil, the insurrection gone
From consciousness have left the man only
A name on weathered stone; a forgotten part
Of gray troops marching and shifting in the dark.

Richmond and Petersburg are names in the night
To travelers, and years of winds have worn away
The smell of smoke from Shenandoah; drowned
The memories of Vicksburg in the river sounds.
He, knowing these names from purgatory, is one
With slow Piedmont waters and pines dropping
Their spear-shaft needles on his speechless head.

Such silence as commends the dead the earth has kept
In him, and binds his body endlessly with roots
Of pine, absolving him by toil of filtered rain.
He is of legend and of history and yet the least
Of misted thousands, gallant with winds and old.
He is of storms at Hatteras, a voice sweeping
Northward in the hurricane and weeping for the dead.

Watching Children

George Zabriskie

Beneath the autumn-altered trees, the homing children
shout release from school: and memory merges these
with our once childish faces and the sound of laughter
from immediate delight of shuffling leaves. The proud
and brave defiant little boys run . . . where?

Down all
the long adventurous streets they cry their furies
and their self-appointed tasks, of messengers and spies
and airmen: only once to know again that same
devotion to a *thing,* and once again to be sure and brave. . . .

They turn from us, their strange obnoxious watchers, who
they think lack comprehension, but the falling
leaves are with us, and the yellow grass, and we are
everywhere
within the parks and down the streets, who feel again
those imminent dangers from fears on the burdensome
trips to the store, the ecstasy of blind braveness.
Our faces, like cracked cups, betray that lost sureness.

And at their mother's supper call they leave us in the cool
silhouetted evening. And as we used to sit at table, they,
small, tired and quarrelsome, eat the food that's urged:
under hard kitchen-lights, the droning of parental voices
flattens their meaning, faces merge with yellow walls,
and carrots and beets color the plates like laughter.

Outside, we turn through smoky streets to faceless rooms.

For H.W.W.

George Zabriskie

Why then, do we assess ourselves with grief,
Because the dead have peace in their return
To earth, and are at once with history and time?
And yet the fresh obituary grass, the stone
Too neatly cut, that mark the grave renew
The wearing memories with resurrected spring.

Because he was a living man, and now is still
Apart from books he loved, apart from dynamos
And flowing solder, and his formulas—
And does not hear our praise, and he ignores
Our arguments, we cannot help remembering
The hot young mind, the strange impetuous
Manners he had:

and we keep listening to hear
Him fingering the loud impatient doorbell: only
Sensing his silence in perpetual earth: perpetual
In spring and summer are the dead, into the earth
Transmuted, and forgetting laughter.

That Beauty Passes Like a Dream

(from "West Durham Winter")

George Zabriskie

On turning axle creaks the year, the old machinery
Of lithographed and gilded calendars the milkman
Brings, the grocer sends: their art and compliments
To grace the home throughout the year where spring
And summer are but numbers now when on the wall
The people hang chronologies of shifting shuttles, reels
Unwinding in the mills. . . .

And they shall hear each day
The trains and whistles, engines shifting cars
Inside the factory yard, and know these link them surely
To worlds they do not know. . . .

The trees shall bear again
The bursting bud, the greening leaf; the roads
Shall dry, bear dust again, and men shall not be cold.
On U. S. Seventy, how many cars shall pass, and trucks
Shall toil up little grades, with whining gears before
The summer comes, how many miles of cloth shall leave
The mills to prove their lives are repetitious and enslaved?
The census takers come, and make the world statistical,
But do not change it: here is no revolt but death,
And even that is ineffectual; the cheap coffin borne
In the crawling hearse, followed by dirty ancient cars
Is witless proof, and standard gravestones add the sin
Of final ugliness. Here thought has lost its sting,
And song is standardized. Yet ineluctable as noise,
Tall leafing trees will hide the houses in the spring.

The Freight Train

(from "Roxboro Street")

George Zabriskie

The Negro leans upon the railroad bridge
To watch the rattling freight go through.

* * *

Many days have touched this place, and hours
Of sun have left the asphalt hot. Smell
The tobacco smell from the warehouse. Now
The train rumbles on the concrete floor;
Smell the engine smell, see the slow smoke
Adumbrate the lazy afternoon. Laughter

Of Negro girls drowns in the train sound,
Black thighs beneath the scarlet skirts
Pattern the cloth with their shadow play.

Over their heads, the freight train rolls,
The box car sides sing American names:
Erie, Southern, Cotton Belt, Coast Line,
Milwaukee, Seaboard, Burlington, Monon.
On the wheels that turn for sleepless miles
A continent rolls above the street,
A continent visits the twisting yards
And leaves again.

In the droning afternoon
Time is like flies, that mate and crawl
On the warehouse wall. White faces streak
Between the black and brown; and Africa

Sings in the blood, in the dark voices
Singing low tunes with darker ancestry.

* * *

By the railroad bridge, the disinherited
Of distant continents wear out their lives.
The blood cooling, their green bright memories
Fading, their history is like the broken tower

Of smoke receding into sky. Time becomes
Dimensionless and meaningless beyond the mind.
With miles and years, eternal Africa has gone;
A shadowy Atlantis, sinking deeper in the brain
Of this black Hamlet, watching the train bend
On eastward tracks and vanish. He, knowing
This afternoon detached from life, can feel
Only the sun, distorting vision on the steel.

Nachtstücke

Lorenz Eitner

Shadows

WHEN NIGHT falls and the good citizen goes home to wife and bed, the world drops its gray mask and reveals its true face, which is darkness and horror. Sometimes it happens that a solid citizen, whose sleep has been disturbed by nightmares, staggers to the bedroom window for fresh air and finds the town with all its roofs and the familiar street below magically transformed. Across a pavement pale with fright, two rows of human heads with dead black eyes and gaping doors glare at each other in impotent hatred. The water in the gutters is black as dried blood, and chimneys reach into the night air like hands of drowning men. Shadows, which have waited in hidden corners and in empty windows during the day, break loose from their walls and inhabit the deserted street. A group of trees stands arm in arm like brothers, and over it, surrounded by black sky, floats the moon and looks down on the citizen who rubs his eyes and suddenly discovers that he has never seen the night before.

Children and animals know the night by instinct and are afraid of the dark.

Salomon and the Seven Half-Moons

"Do come in! I am so pleased you came! The others are already waiting inside. I am so happy that you have come! Here, let me take off your coat. Welcome, welcome among us! Yes, the Swami is already here. We should be so thankful that He has sent him here. Verily, disciples will come from afar, as the prophet says, and the Good Cause will thrive. I am so, so glad to have you with us!" Miss Sally Weaver, the Keeper of the Keys, turned a pair of watery eyes heavenward, clutched the guest's coat to her bosom, and carried it away in triumph.

The disciples were sitting in the living room. A lone candle burned in a plaster-of-Paris skull grinning placidly in the middle of the tablecloth. The Swami, a dark little man in an ill-fitting tuxedo, sat at the head of the table. At his right was throned Dr. Boller in the full regalia of a Grand Knight of the Mystic Order of Salomon and the Seven Half-Moons. At the Swami's left sat Miss Nattie Kummel, the Keeper of the Sacred Books. The other knights, mostly elderly ladies, whispered to each other. One chair stood empty: the Keeper of the Keys was still busy in the cloak room. In the background hung a reproduction of Dürer's "Knight, Death, and Devil," surrounded by potted palms.

Finally the Keeper of the Keys glided in, throwing victorious smiles about. The Grand Knight, who had been staring at his fingernails with sad eyes, swallowed nervously, rose to his feet, and began to read from a piece of cardboard, which he held in his hollow hand close to his eyes:

"Brothers and Sisters! 'The world is in travail,' saith the prophet, 'and its agitation waxeth day by day. Its face is turned towards waywardness and unbelief. Such shall be its plight that to disclose it now would not be meet and seemly. Its perversity will long continue. And when the appointed hour is come, there shall suddenly appear that which shall cause the limbs of mankind to quake. The Knights of Salomon will come from the East and drive the Red and the Black Lion into the waters of the West. Then and only then will the Divine Standard be unfurled and the Nightingale of Paradise warble its melody.' "

"So shall it be!" whispered the Keeper of the Sacred Books fervently and looked about with pious fish-eyes.

"Tonight, Brothers and Sisters, we have among us one who has been guided into our midst from afar. It is the Swami Samsanavatna Lahore, who has traveled through the countries of the Orient and the Occident with the famous Lundgreen Brothers Circus as phrenologist, mindreader, spiritualist, and fakir. The Swami has consented to establish contact between this gathering and some dear departed spirit above. I feel it to be my duty to express my sincerest gratitude to the Swami in behalf of our exalted brotherhood."

The Swami arose, rubbed his hands with professional agility, and said: "Thnack you. Plneaze brinck the medium in."

The Keeper of the Keys hurried out and returned with a round-shouldered, pimple-faced youth. The Swami pushed the medium into a chair and executed magnetic strokes about his temples. The round-shouldered youth sat relaxed with closed eyes and sagging mouth. It was so silent in the room that the ticking of wrist watches became audible.

Time passed. The potted palms stood motionless and the grinning plaster-of-Paris skull gave dim light. The Knights of Salomon sat woven into a web of black arms, legs, and bodies and white, expectant faces.

Slowly a pale, bluish fluorescence developed, apparently with some effort, in the darkness above the medium's bowed head. Slowly it unfolded like a floating veil, spread, and shrank, and grew gradually into a round, luminous space with uneven dark spots. Even to the most skeptical of the knights it looked like the blurred image of a human face.

"Sister Agnes!" gasped someone.

A stirring went through the potted palms, and from a great distance a voice became audible.

"I am speaking from the spirit woild and it is beautiful up here with clouds and harp music and them angels flying around and Christ sitting at the Right of the Lord as it is written in the Scriptures. Day and night we sing His praise. And I always keep thinking of you, specially of you, sister Nattie and you, Sister Sally, and we hear all your prayers and carry them up before His throne. And I could tell you a lot of things only we spirits aren't allowed to. Don't be afraid of death. You don't feel nothing. And then all of a sudden you are up here, and nothing has changed, and you look just as always, only you have cast away the bonds of the body and walk in the spirit. And my arthritis is gone. And we always . . . we always . . . we always . . . we always. . . ."

A cold draft cut through the room. The potted palms rustled. Above the medium's head the fluorescence trembled, folded up, and faded into a flickering streak.

The round-shouldered youth gave a long sigh and awoke. Slowly the black knots of legs, arms, and bodies dissolved into separate knights. The faces were still pale.

The Concert

My name is Pernath; I am a retired musician. I live at Number 17 Bertholdi Street, at the corner of the Old Green Market, four creaky flights high, directly under the sloping roof of a house that belongs to the Widow Goldleaf.

In this room which measures hardly five yards from wall to wall, I have spent the last twenty-one years, by choice rather than because of poverty, for my pension and the monies which my mother left me when she died would be sufficient for more sumptuous lodgings. Once I lived in a small house in the suburbs. I remember that it had a flower and kitchen garden and even a small artificial grotto in the backyard. But that was long ago, before my wife left me. Since then I have lived at the Widow Goldleaf's. My room is dark and somewhat moist, but I have become so accustomed to its cool twilight that I am determined not to give it up.

A painful nervous condition which makes me extremely sensitive to strong light and noise forces me to sleep during the day and to arise only after sundown. I wait patiently until it has grown quite dark and the last car has rattled through Bertholdi Street. When the gas lanterns have been lit by the same ageless man who used to light them with his pole twenty-one years ago, I leave the house and walk down the darker side of the street where I do not have to fear the glare of the lanterns until I turn to the left into a narrow side street. At the end of this street is "The Wild Man," where I take my only meal. The distance between the house of the Widow Goldleaf and the Wild Man is 246 paces. I count my steps automatically as I walk and am pleased that their number remains always the same. At the Wild Man I am received by the old waiter, who is, I believe, the proprietor of the establishment. His wife cooks in the kitchen. I have never seen any guests there. The old waiter is now quite deaf; for many years we have not spoken a single word. My meal is always the same. It consists of soft, digestible foods, for my teeth are not strong, and a glass of wine to stimulate the circulation of the blood.

After the meal I walk the 246 steps back to the house of the Widow Goldleaf, on the darker side of the street. In my room I light only two candles for economical reasons and prepare three more to be lighted when the guests arrive. Then I sit down in my armchair and doze for a while. Outside, the neighboring roofs lie like black mountains in the moonlight. Some windows are lighted, and I can see Mr. Schmidt in slippers and robe reading the evening paper while his wife is mending socks.

About midnight there is loud knocking at the door. I light the three candles and watch the castrate pushing his enormous figure through my narrow door. The castrate is soprano at the opera. He calls himself Artaria, but I believe that that is not his real name. I have known him for more than thirty years now. When I still played for the opera, he was almost my only friend. He visits me every night after the performance, often with traces of greasepaint about his face and powder in his hair, and is now my only contact with the world. His body is immense, his head very small, and his voice high and clear like that of a child. We shake hands solemnly, and he stands stooped over me under the low ceiling and looks at me with his very old, childlike face while he unpacks his violin. After a while the two others arrive with their instruments. They are friends of the castrate and, I think, musicians at the opera.

Every night we play quartets together. Artaria is our first violin. When the music becomes very beautiful he often cries, silently, with large tears rolling down his face. Thus we play for many hours.

Finally the two musicians leave, and Artaria, too, puts his violin away and bows out through my narrow door.

I am sorry to see him go. He is my only contact with the world (I do not count the Widow Goldleaf and the waiter at the Wild Man).

The Demon

Willy was so demonic that it was really quite embarrassing. He was hollow-cheeked and dark-eyed and had carefully tangled black locks. When he entered a restaurant, cloaked in black, the brim of a soft black hat pressed down over his forehead, and cast his diabolical glances about, waiters dropped their trays, dogs misbehaved, children cried, and fat gentlemen stopped their coffee cups in mid-air and stared with protruding eyeballs.

Willy had always been a professional demon. He had begun his career as ballet dancer and startled audiences with his satanic creations accompanied by somber tom-tom rhythms. Since long hair would have disturbed the lines of his dance, he had shaved his skull and painted a large red circle on his powdered forehead.

Finally the censor banned his conception of "Death and the Maiden," and Willy appeared in court with his red circle, dressed apparently in nothing but a loose black raincoat.

When it became necessary to find another means of lucrative self-expression, Willy grew hair, dyed it green like Baudelaire's, and founded a new literary movement under the battlecry *"Vive la Decadence."*

The neglected geniuses of the hollow-eyed and flat-chested profession flocked about him. Willy rented a garret, furnished it with a skull, a straw sack, and an oriental prayer rug. The literati came to his garret and brought with themselves poetry, tubercular coughs, and occasional delirium tremens.

After several weeks Willy sent the prayer rug to a dry cleaner and a thin manuscript to the printer. It was the decadent manifesto entitled *From the Gallows.* Bound neatly in human skin and printed on genuine papyrus, it finally appeared and was praised by the critical press (Willy under various pseudonymous disguises). Willy's picture appeared in the literary supplements and frightened the unsuspecting readers. They represented him dressed in tweedy garments of his own invention, something resembling a fireman's helmet drawn over his head, his pale face with the terrible eyes framed by a seven-pointed beard.

Quite suddenly a great spiritual change came over Willy. He read the Upanishads and renounced this world. Forty days and nights he fasted in his garret and repeated ceaselessly all the sacred prayers which he had learned by heart. After this purgatory period, he felt himself refreshed in spirit and body and decided to walk through the streets of the city nude as God had created him to preach repentance to the people.

Considerable crowds gathered and stared, and the police

tried in vain to arrest him. There and then the Spirit spoke in Willy and commanded him to preach to the multitude. And he shook his tangled black locks, raised his arms commanding silence, and spoke, while someone passed around a hat. And it was horrible to hear him preach in free verse, and the crowd knelt in the street and repented—although they did not understand a word. The collection netted him $53.75, and Willy gave up ballet and literature and founded a new church.

The Sound of Eternity

Elizabeth Dilts Kibbee

EDWARD looked at his orange juice with distaste. "Oh, all right!" he said. He drank it quickly and scowled; then he kissed Victoria and went to the chair in the living room where his coat and books were.

"Do you have your glasses?" she called. "And your lunch money?"

He dropped a "Yeah!" and left it hanging there as he dashed out.

Miriam finished her cereal. Her face looked childishly puffy, the way it always did in the morning. She stood, stretched, kissed Victoria, said, "Bye, Mother," and left. Nathan had gone nearly an hour ago; he had finished his coffee and said, "At eight o'clock on Monday morning, teaching is a noble profession." So Victoria was alone with the breakfast dishes and her second cup of coffee and the morning sunshine across the table.

She went into the living room and took two cigarettes out of the box on the coffee table. Going back to the breakfast room, she thought, Mrs. Donne didn't have tobacco to fall back on. She wondered about coffee. Hello, Mrs. Donne, would you like a second cup of coffee? Won't you join us, Mrs. Carlyle? No, really, there's plenty. You don't have to worry; we have eternity. Canby said Nathan's book had the sound of eternity. It was in the *Saturday Review* last week—did you happen to read it?

The other reviews were favorable, too—the *Times* and the *Tribune,* even the *New Yorker,* and the *Publishers' Weekly* and the *Atlantic.* The local *Clarion* was good, of course, and the New York Sunday editions, then the weeklies and the monthlies. Gentlemen and scholars all: "Classic," they pronounced. "After *Stephen Finney* and *Blood of Battle,* Nathan Ewing's latest offering establishes him as one of the leading literary figures of the twentieth century." And Canby said, "Nathan Ewing has the sound of eternity."

"The sound of eternity," Victoria said to the coffee pot. College catalogues would say, "English 205: Twentieth-Century Prose. Proust, Joyce, D. H. Lawrence, Ewing." And there would be ninety-five-cent editions in the second-hand bookshop. Eternity: maybe even a separate course. Maybe two terms. What is your field, Doctor? The twentieth century. I wrote my dissertation on Ewing. . . . Brilliant fellow—follower of Ewing. Leading authority on Ewing.

The doorbell rang; it was the laundryman. She gave him the bundle and returned a sock they'd sent last week by mistake. "Thank you, Mrs. Ewing," the man said. She smiled and watched him go down the sidewalk. Be careful of those shirts, she thought of saying. And those sheets. Eternity sleeps on those sheets. The man threw the bundle into the truck and drove to the next house. Victoria returned to her coffee and toast. Hello, Mrs. Johnson, she said silently, lifting her cup. Does Samuel wear as many shirts a week as Nathan? I have to tell them not to starch the collars.

She put out her cigarette and stacked the dishes. Spring was beginning; remember to get Jason to fix the lawn and spade the garden when it thawed. But no—not this year. She looked out of the kitchen window at the trees and thought, with a sort of rueful triumph, Congratulations, Victoria. You forgot it for nearly ten hours. Ten hours without considering what should be shipped first or what to do about the golf clubs. Nathan's biographer—he would have a biographer, of course—would say, "In 1940 Ewing left his post at the University and went to New York to take up the editorship of the *Columbian*." He would not add that they went to the city in February to find an apartment and that Mrs. Ewing wore herself out packing the family's worldly goods and arranging for the children's transfer to a new school and shuddered at the thought of entertaining urban literati. In *Who's Who* it would sound so simple: "Ewing, Nathan . . . Instructor, Assistant Professor, Associate Professor of English, Fleet University, 1932-40; editor, the *Columbian*, 1940- ." Well, other people moved, other people who were Who, and, for that matter, people who were not: people who would get old, die, and be tombstones, instead of Eternal. Don't feel bad about it, you tombstones. You helped us a lot. You did our laundry and spaded our gardens and took care of the children while we went to banquets; furthermore, you moved our furniture and bought our books (a few of you) and shook hands with us and became characters in our stories. You see? We are making you Eternal, too. Be a

Character, and you too can be the life of the party.

She put the dishes away and went upstairs to make the beds. She did Edward's first because his room was always the worst, his clothes puddles of disorder on the floor, model aeroplane parts strewn over his desk and dresser. The solid models were the worst, because they entailed whittling. Two finished models were on top of the bookshelf, delicate, paper-covered things. And how are we going to get those to New York? Victoria thought in sudden consternation. And if we don't, how are we going to appease Edward? She sighed and hung his pajamas in the closet.

Edward had said, "Mother, we won't have a yard, will we?"

"No," she had said, and, "We'll miss it, won't we?"

"Yeah. . . ." Period of reflection; then, "Mother, when I get so I can find my way around New York pretty well, I'm going to get Carl to come and visit me. We can go out to LaGuardia Field and watch the planes all day. Can we, Mother?"

" 'May we.' We'll see when we get settled. There'll be such a lot of things we can do."

Yes, you have the idea, Edward. Forget about the yard and the Dorothy Perkins roses and badminton tournaments in the summer and swimming in the University pool on Wednesdays. Victoria went into Miriam's room. And Miriam, with her piano lessons and her little compositions, she added to herself. Miriam, with the beginnings of beauty and long, mysterious daydreams; she will grow into a glamour girl from a medium-priced novel. Well, maybe not; but *Who's Who* would say merely, "Children: Edward Nash and Miriam Carlton."

Yes, and I'll have a notice, too, she added, going into the master bedroom. "Married, 1930, Victoria Carlton." Period. Well, that's all that matters. They couldn't say, could they, that Victoria was secretary to a professor, and Nathan went to see him, but he wasn't in, so Nathan had to come back, and he and the professor's secretary—that's me, folks—got to talking and went out to dinner together, and then—no; no, that wouldn't do. It will even make, Victoria thought a little sadly, tiring reading in the biography. Boy meets girl, boy gets girl—no complications. A biographer would not even take the trouble to figure out that Nathan had been gentle and thoughtful always, that he made love with the same concentrated care he used when he faced a class or established a theory or worked on a novel. No, that's something eternity won't bother about. If there were an illicit love affair, it would be different. They'd publish letters. No, the sophomores of eternity, if they gave it any thought, would probably think that Nathan Ewing, personally, was a dud. She could hear a sophomoric voice saying, "Dull tool!" But Eternity would, of course, date that expression. She must remember to save them a good picture for the biography, because Nathan was good-looking, in a way, with deepset eyes and a heavy sort of head and thick hair.

She went downstairs and stood uncertainly in the hall. She had to start packing today, because the movers would come in a week. Some things would have to be stored. She went to the big catch-all closet under the stairs and began taking things out. They were dusty, after standing all winter—summer things, the badminton set and the tennis rackets and the picnic equipment. Badminton and picnics and sunshine and polo shirts and bare legs would be

out in New York. This comes in the course of a great man's life, Victoria reasoned, sneezing as she brought a box down from the shelf. Did you want him to be stuck here for the rest of his life? Come on, now, Mrs. Ewing, a little pride, there—that's right. After all, this is part of the clutch for Eternity, this moving to the Mecca of the literary world. It's like typing the master's thesis in that hot little room in a boarding house. Hello, Mrs. Boswell; did Jamie take graduate work in summer school? Was it the hottest summer on record, and did you have a furnished room under a tin roof? We don't know, Mrs. Boswell; they don't tell us things like that. Was there a Mrs. Boswell? See—we don't know, and there probably was—a nice, dutiful little wife, somewhere in the background. Mrs. Coleridge, did Samuel stay up all night writing, ever, and then have a headache and cut his classes the next day?

Victoria decided to take the tennis things and part of the picnic kit. She stacked them accordingly. The people next door could have the croquet set and the garden tools. They were nice people, tombstones, ultimately, but good neighbors none the less. In their family history they could record that they had been good friends of Nathan Ewing—*the* Nathan Ewing. And you, the skinny lady in the hopeless hat, who were you? I was his wife. Nathan Ewing's wife! How does it feel to be the wife of a great author? Well, it was fun, and Nathan helped a lot.

Victoria surveyed the piles of boxes—this for the movers, that for the neighbors. Moving more slowly than when she was working, she took her old polo coat, the one she couldn't take to New York, and put it on. Then she lit a cigarette and went out into the chill east wind, over to the birdbath at the edge of the yard. She leaned against it and smoked.

Yes it was fun. You can tell them it was fun. It was worth it. Wasn't it worth it, Mrs. Donne? Typing the manuscripts (until he got an amanuensis) and moving and getting up for early breakfasts before the eight o'clocks and the cold house in Osnabrück during the leave-of-absence and Nathan's headaches when he worked all night, all of it, even without Eternity.

But before I die, thought Victoria, shivering a little in the wind, before I die I'm going to write it down. I owe it to them, Mrs. Dickens and Mrs. More and Mrs. Galsworthy—the sewing circle of Eternity, the ones they don't know about because they kept their husbands' shirts in order and brought up their families. I'm going to say that I didn't want to go to New York, too.

It was almost spring, and the sunlight warmed her shoulders and the top of her hair, and her mind became pleasantly vacant. I shall stand here as long as I want to, she said to herself. I don't think I shall pack any more today. She knew, of course, that she would begin on the upstairs storage closet when her cigarette was smoked.

A Dead Girl

Kiffin Rockwell Hayes

Where sparks fly upward from the rolling plain
Between the Appalachian and the sea
You caught the restless sorrow in your heart,
The wind's sad singing in the mountain pines
And the unceasing grieving of the sea.

Being compounded of sea, fire, and air,
What could the spirit do but madly cry,
Locked in the body, teased by body's cares?

The heart shrinks, fearing never to be free,
And envies the tired circling of the bird
Whose heart can soar until slow pinions droop,
But human heart is weak, and cannot hold
The rage that flows within the walls of blood.
And mind outruns old teaching in desire
To seek the unpermitted, and to know
The long-forgotten or the never-known.

You feared to live imprisoned, but no fear
Of aught untested tamed your injured soul,
And now your body melts into the earth;
Your soul sings in the pines, chants in the sea.

A Poem for Lee Happ

Lieutenant, U.S.M.C.R., killed on Saipan, June, 1944.

Kiffin Rockwell Hayes

You cannot draw his face, but you remember
The bony features, certainly not handsome
But showing no defect, the Adam's apple,
The lanky form, less graceful than a maple
But well trained, and something of the manner
Of a big dog almost grown up,
A colt not quite a stallion, full of blood
But handled well to bring out all his grace;
And something of a racer's nervousness
And the disdain for others less than equal.
He had a polish and a way of speaking,
Manners much too good; it was not surprising—
He knew it, you suppose—
He made quick enemies among the vulgar.

It would not be justice to call him a great man,
A doubtful license to hail him young Apollo.
Say he was better than his generation,
Gently-behaved, intelligent, and witty.

The shock is to find him dead, and being dead
In battle, far way, and leading soldiers,
Falling in the adventure of a landing;
Buried so far from home, among those comrades—
Men whom he stood among, and led, respected;
Being perhaps the only gentleman,
By unnatural selection, among these men.
The only one who knew the later poets,

And something of the ancient, a scholar.
It is a shock to find him here, and dead.

Now, having made his polite, last departure
With dignity, old-fashioned, he bequeathes
To our benevolence a ponderable question,
To weigh our survival against an honest death.
It is the question he will not have to answer.

You will not riddle the value of Life itself
Or compare grace with labor, arts with works;
It is useless to ask if he died well
When all the victories he fought are gained.
That is a question to answer for all the dead.

But ask yourself, having known this one man,
Whether or no to breed and train more like him.
Demand the worth of being a gentleman.
And when you have decided, if you decide,
What will you do with them then?
Having made them young and eager,
Courteous, read, given to impractical thinking,
Loving the past and music, remembering names

Of fathers and their customs and their greatness.
Or if you give them leisure, games, and dancing,
Luxury, property more than another's
Until perhaps they seem not so deserving

As lucky, but not abusive of their fortune—
For you would find it hard to keep them true—
Give them good hearts, not leave them empty-headed—
Then you must ask again, what to do with these children,
Too intelligent, precociously polite,
And good for nothing, except to be leaders of men.

[Paris, Lorraine, Luxembourg, Belgium, December, 1944]

Of These Things We Do Not Speak

Edgar C. Greene

TIM WONDERED vaguely as he pulled on the new work pants and shoes what it would be like. It's funny, he told himself. I've got a father and two brothers working in the plant. I've been around auto factories all my life. And yesterday I stood while the foreman showed me the job I was to have, but still this morning it feels new.

As he shaved, Tim wondered about that, too. His brothers never shaved before they went to work. Then with a quick, nervous stroke, he cut himself. He stopped and looked carefully in the mirror for a moment, and then, laughing lightly, he shrugged and washed the lather off his face and went downstairs into the kitchen, feeling foolish.

"Eat your cereal, Tim. Bacon and eggs coming up," said his mother.

"Right," he answered, picking up a spoon.

In a moment his mother came in carrying a plate heavy with food. She sat down and pushed the plate across the table.

"Well?" she said affectionately.

Tim looked up from the cereal and smiled.

"I don't know," he said. Then he looked at the plate. "Do I look like a horse?"

"You'll need it before the day's over. You're working now."

Tim smiled again.

"How do you think you'll like it?" asked his mother.

"Funny. I really don't know. Dad and the boys never say much about it."

"I know. Even when they first started work they never talked much about the plant. I guess they don't think about it."

"I suppose I won't mind it. I'm used to the noise pretty well from just being around it so much. I've got an easy job, too."

"Yes. Your father had to push a yankee drill when he went to work. I don't guess you'll get too tired, because your father never complained at all."

"Uh-huh," mumbled Tim through a mouthful of coffee.

When he finished eating, he lit a cigarette and pushed back his chair. He didn't get up, though, just sat smoking and smiling at his mother, who was smiling back. They sat that way for nearly a minute, and then Tim got up.

"Guess I'll be running. It's getting late."

"Yes."

They walked to the front door. Tim put his hand on the knob.

"I wish I didn't have the odd shift. Then I could go in the car with the rest of them."

"Yes. Goodbye, Tim."

"Goodbye." Tim waved as he walked down the street.

His mother stood in the doorway until he was out of sight. The air was brisk and she shivered a little. Tim was her youngest. He had just turned eighteen. She'd hoped for something better for him.

Tim walked with his hands in his pockets, rocking on the thick new leather soles. If I only didn't have the odd shift, he thought nervously. Then I could ask my father or Bill or Jim. Jim, I could say, how is it? Do you—will I like it? And then he could tell me and that would be all of it right there.

Tim covered the six blocks to the factory quickly, walking fast—a little eagerly—to keep warm. His face was red and flaky-looking as he finally walked up to the factory and into the oblivion of the multitude. Yet even as he passed the iron gate and started for his section of the line he felt terrifically alone—individual—subconsciously proud. He was perfectly silent amid the still noise of rustling denim, broken only by the sound of voices from the *white collar* office over to the left.

"Good morning," he said to the foreman as he came into the shop. He didn't look at the foreman when he spoke; and the foreman, counting the men as they came in, answered absently and didn't look at Tim. The metal tinkle of the numbered checks as the men drew out their tools was the only other sound. Tim took his brush, glass of turpentine, and bucket of silver paint and walked over to the first unpainted motor on the line. Pulling up the battery box on which he was to sit, he began daubing at the motor, dipping the brush carefully in the paint.

At precisely this moment the siren sounded and the line began to move. As the echoes of this starting wail died away, the clashing grind of the metal lathes began screeching on the floor above. In the next room the rushing hiss of the torches leaped into the jumble of sound as the welders began work, and thus all over the plant the noise of machinery rose to its crescendo and held.

Tim showed no sign of having noticed the outburst but simply began slapping his brush more vigorously at the row of unpainted motors streaming relentlessly toward him. Rather, the noise drowned the room with a weight that seemed to hang perilously about Tim's head, pressing eagerly around his consciousness, biting queerly at the motions of his moving arm.

He carefully studied the bolt heads protruding from the sockets above each cylinder, taking care that they were entirely covered with paint. Carefully, oh, ever so meticulously, he watched the bolts in their sockets moving slowly but irrevocably past. Carefully—each bolt—then carefully the many bolts and hundreds of sockets and thousands of bolts and sockets and bolts and sockets until the movement of his brush from bucket to motor to bolt to socket—indeed his whole being itself—merged with the flow of the line and the movements of the other men and the noise until there was no longer a Tim or a brush or a bolt or a line but merely a huge whole, working—co-ordinating smoothly—perfectly, spewing finished units from the debris of raw materials.

* * * * *

. . . Gradually. Bit by bit . . . a portion to each man, from this multicomposed entity, disturbing not the solidi-

fied pervading atmosphere of smoke and noise and torch flashes, rose those other bodies of men. The ethereal, uncharted and invisible things, born of the gray innards of the skull—detached from the material earth and yet somehow engulfing it with their omnipotence. The mental drippings of men—lost in unison like men asleep at night. The last vestiges of individuality. Each a stream of thought reaching away to some strange mystery of power far away and yet strangely near and pressing.

Each a separate thing.

. . . tonight I will kill him . . . seize him and beat him . . . crunching bone and gushing blood and putty flesh . . . see . . . maybe you won't be so rash . . . bah . . . sniveler . . . tonight your time is up, for I'll kill you . . . Goddamn you . . . yes, you, and if you've got any friends, Goddamn them too . . . tonight I'll kill you. . . .

. . . Tony, you are a wonderful singer. I, Tony, am like Caruso many, many times . . . beautiful music and lilting arias . . . singing violins . . . white-fronted people swarming at me . . . disdaining . . . Vienna and Munich and Rome . . . yes . . . and even perhaps New York . . . but beautiful notes and melody . . . Rigoletto . . . la donna è mobile . . . Carmen . . . toreador . . . toreador . . . Tibbet and Caruso, yes and Pons and all . . . all me . . . l'opéra . . . Tony Manaci and Caruso and Rigoletto. . . .

. . . I am wonderful. All the Lotharios of the ages in one . . . my muscles are strong and tireless as I go laughing, bubbling about the romantic places, being big and doing wonders—island of the Caribbean . . . Guam—Malay—Zanzibar . . . all of the beautiful girls in all of the world are all in love with me. They worship me but I am the

one . . . the great . . . only . . . and I take of each and harbor none closely or tightly. . . .

. . . yeah . . . sure . . . I'm a nigger . . . so what . . . niggers are all right . . . I'm just like you . . . two arms . . . two legs . . . a nose . . . only you're white and I'm black . . . it doesn't make any difference . . . it won't make any difference . . . time goes on and it won't make any difference to anybody. . . .

. . . you're lovely, Betty . . . lovely . . . I love you, Betty. . . .

. . . Christmas . . . money . . . bills . . . money. . . .

. . . all afternoon and morning . . . work . . . the line . . . yes. . . .

. . . I wonder . . . if it's a boy, I'll give money to the church . . . if it is . . . but it must be . . . I don't like girls . . . if it's a boy, I'll give. . . .

. . . I'm old . . . the years come tumbling . . . old. . . .

. . . it takes time, Martha . . . too much time . . . I'm afraid. . . .

As the line had started moving, so it stopped at the sound of the siren. The noise of the plant ceased as quickly as it had begun, leaving the phantom image of smoke and clatter momentarily framed in the sudden silence. Tim looked at the head of the bolt on the motor before him and after assuring himself that it was completely covered, picked up his brush, glass of turpentine, slightly filled paint bucket and checked them in the stock room. Flexing the muscles in his arms and legs, Tim walked out of the shop through the yard, past the iron gate.

He wasn't as tired as he had thought he might be. Instead he felt himself filled with an inward glow, refreshed, at ease. As the mass of men began to thin, he looked at the man walking on his right on the sidewalk. The man was one of the workers from his section of the line. They walked along side by side. The man never looked at him; but at the second corner, when he turned off, Tim imagined that he nodded slightly.

Tim held his head high and walked erect. His father and two brothers passed him in the car. They were on their way to work. He waved happily to them and began to walk slower, feeling the sunshine. He was faintly conscious of having made a transition in life. He knew he belonged. He was no longer just Tim. And mixed closely with his calm elation was the impression of having been for a moment near something bigger than anything he had ever known.

Reaching the house, Tim walked up on the porch and began fumbling for his key. He opened the door and then, stooping to pick up the evening paper, walked into the hall and down it into the living room, where he sat down and began looking at the headlines.

Almost immediately his mother appeared in the doorway.

"Well, Tim?" she said expectantly. "How did you like it? Did everything go all right?"

"All right? Yes. Everything went all right. Yes. It was O. K., I guess."

Tim turned the pages of the paper looking for the comics. Finding them, he leaned back in the chair, lit a cigarette, and began reading about the little orphan girl who could never seem to keep out of trouble.

His mother stood in the doorway watching him—waiting. After a moment, she shook her head a little—resignedly—and with a shrug went out into the kitchen and began rattling pots and pans.

The Long Shadows

Donald Thompson

"HENRY!" The woman's voice, whining yet harsh, reached quite clearly to the boy sitting on the steps, but he did not move. "Henry!" At the second summons he stirred, lifted one brogan-shod foot a step higher, but made no motion to respond.

"Henry, I got to have some water right now!" This time the petulant voice was followed by heavy footsteps, and a hot, frowsy-looking woman appeared at the door. She was of medium height, but her body was covered with layer upon layer of fat. There was evidence of a "permanent" in the dark hair which clung moistly to her head—not, however, a very recent one. Her fat, hairy legs were bare, her feet thrust into soiled and shapeless slippers. She wore a wrinkled cotton house dress, shorter by an inch than her faded pink slip, one strap of which hung down her right arm. Her abdomen, enlarged by five months' preg-

nancy, bulked beneath a flour-sack apron. She was still young—in her middle twenties, perhaps, but the traces of what might have been a rather attractive youthful prettiness were fading fast in her ever-heavier features.

"Henry, you know I cain't worsh without no water." Her voice was as usual shrill, but with a little pleading note in it now.

The boy on the steps eased his blue-jeaned buttocks from the top step onto the porch and resettled his back against the post on which he was leaning. Taking from a pocket of his blue chambray shirt a small cloth bag, he rolled himself one of the cigarettes which were to him a symbol of his newly acquired sixteen-year-old manhood. He lit it and took two or three deep drags before he answered. "Bertie, you know good 'n' well I been workin' all day; ain't set down since breakfast till now. And I ain't goin' to git you no water till I rest a while." His tone was quiet, mildly but unmistakably defiant.

Sensing his mood, the woman in the door said nothing in reply but pushed open the screen door and started to step out on the porch. Then she hesitated and let the screen slam shut while she stood still behind it, watching a fly crawl up the other side. She changed the subject: "I wish you'd git busy an' kill some o' these ol' flies while you're restin', Henry. They jist worry a body to death." She came out on the porch.

Henry watched the approach of his stepmother, who said, "You ought to git me some water, honey, so I c'n have some clean clothes for you an' your daddy to wear." She leaned over him and punched his shoulder with pretended playfulness. The top of her dress was unbuttoned, and he could see her huge white breasts spilling out of her slip. She followed his eyes, and seeing that he saw, grinned shyly but made no attempt to fasten her dress.

"Damn milk-factories," he thought. "Why does she keep showin' 'em to me?" And he thought of the night, a couple of months before, when his father had been away. She'd called to him from the bedroom to bring her a glass of water, and when he'd taken it to her she was lying there naked on the bed, grinning at him. It was something like that all the time; he'd been staying with his father and this new "mother" for only three months, and already he was sick of it and wanted to leave.

He jerked his shoulder away from her touch, but she sat down beside him on the porch. "Ain't you goin' to do jist one little thing for me, Henry? I'm askin' you jist as nice as I know how." She leaned toward him, and he felt her body hot against his. When he looked at her, she was grinning at him.

"Oh, all right, Bertie!" He got up quickly, almost upsetting her as he moved. Snapping away the half-smoked cigarette, he exhaled a last lungful of smoke. For some reason he noticed its queer dead grayish color and the contrast it made with the hot clear blue of the sky, the cool green darkness of the woods across the road. "Gimme the buckets," he said wearily, "an' I'll bring you a load before dinner. What're we gonna have to eat, anyway? I'm awful hungry."

"Oh, I don't know." Bertie's voice expressed more satisfaction at getting her way about the water than concern over his hunger. "I thought I'd jist warm up some o' that cornbread an' the beans we had last night, an' we got some pork from breakfast this mornin'." She got up heavily and went into the house after the buckets. When she came back he took them without a word and started down the hill, a gleaming zinc pail in either hand.

Instead of going through the gate, he followed along the fence to the place where he always climbed over, except that when he came back with the water, he would have to use the gate then. It was nearly half a mile to the Higgins place, where the water was, so he didn't hurry. It was an awful lot of trouble to get water, but, like working, it offered an escape from Bertie. His father usually got water with the car, a milk-can full every night, but they always ran out when Bertie washed, and he had to carry more.

The road felt soft beneath his heavy shoes, and Henry wished he were barefoot, so he could feel the pleasant, warm, snuff-colored dirt between his toes. He longed to hop slowly along on one foot, as he had used to do, dragging the back of his toes along the surface of the road. It made his instep tingle pleasurably just to think about it. He had an impulse to stop and take off his shoes, but he was afraid somebody might come along the road and see him. He had to remember that he was sixteen now and almost old enough to join the Navy; his father had already promised to sign the papers next year, in spite of Bertie's objections. It made him feel good to think that his father didn't always take up for Bertie—at least not about important things.

Thinking about his father and Bertie reminded him of his mother, who had died when he was very young. He didn't remember very much about her, except that she had been good to him. He remembered that she was tall and lovely and kind—not at all like Bertie. From somewhere back in the depths of his memory came a picture of a tall, brown-haired woman in a green dress, with some sort of open-work down the long sleeves. There was on his cheek the dimly remembered feel of that dress, the fabric's dainty roughness good to the sensitive skin. He seemed to sense in his nostrils the clean, sweet smell of the cloth and of her, perhaps of some faint perfume she wore. Then he thought of Bertie's big, sweaty body; he shuddered; and the picture and the memory were gone.

That was the way all the time, he thought—any time when he was enjoying himself, even if it was only by thinking about something pleasant, Bertie always spoiled it, one way or another. He hadn't really felt happy a single minute since he'd been living in her house. He would rather be back with the Gordons, even, on the farm where he had spent most of the ten years since his mother died, "farmed out" by a father who had no place to take him. Yes, it would be better even to be back there, with all the cursing and beating and the hard, back-breaking work in the fields. He could especially remember the south corn field, with its quarter-mile-long rows of tall green stalks. How many times the sun had beat down upon his back and the green blades had cut his face as he hoed slowly down one row and back another! Compared with that, the little work he had to do now, tending a few acres of truck, was more like play, or getting a vacation.

When he said "play" in his mind, he smiled bitterly to himself, as if it were some sort of secret joke on him that he'd grown up almost without knowing what play is. Certainly he'd had little opportunity for it on the Gordon farm; his days had been filled with labor and his nights with sleep and dreams of getting away. So now he was away, and he thought of going back! But he couldn't just run away; that wouldn't be fair to his father. It would all have been so much simpler if his father had married somebody else when he bought this little farm. Even Cora, who'd been his first stepmother, before Bertie, would have been better. She was hard to get along with, but he liked her better than Bertie. At least she was clean and not fat, and not always messing around with him.

Down one last little hill, through the creaking gate at the bottom, and he was at the Higgins spring. He set down the buckets on the worn gray boards of the spring house floor and squatted down beside them to thrust his hands and forearms into the clear, cold water. Then he took off the battered straw hat which shielded his head from the hot summer sun and stretched out full length on the boards. Thrusting his whole face into the water, he held it there for a long time, letting it cool his face and forehead, drinking in great mouthfuls of it, and lifting his head only when he could hold his breath no longer.

He had just raised his head when he heard a step and looked up to discover that he was no longer alone. "Oh, hello, Ruth Ann." There was mingled relief and embarrassment in his tone. He was glad, though, that it wasn't anyone else; he didn't mind her being around. Ruth Ann Higgins was a year older that he, and was, he thought, the prettiest and nicest girl he'd ever seen; she was the only one he'd ever talked to. He never had liked girls; they were always giggling and acting silly or else trying to flirt with you. All but Ruth Ann, that is. He didn't know her very well, and he never saw her except sometimes when he came after water. He had told her that he wasn't going to school any more, now that he was sixteen, and she'd tried to get him to change his mind.

He wasn't sure just what he ought to say now, so he got up and wiped his mouth with the back of his hand and put on his straw hat. Then he said again, "Hello," lamely, and waited for her to speak. She had sat down on the large flat rock that formed one side of the spring and was looking at him, her large blue eyes calm and clear when they met his.

"Hello, Henry." She looked down at her hands, moved them to smooth a wrinkle in the large skirt of her black-and-white checked gingham dress, and then folded them in her lap. He watched her in silence, vaguely disturbed; he hadn't really known she was quite so pretty as she looked now. Her long brown hair was tied by a small white ribbon at the back of her neck; it framed a face unfreckled by the summer sun, without makeup, made interesting by the good line of the chin, the high cheekbones, and the tilted nose. Her dress looked as if it were fresh from the ironing board; it fitted snugly from the waist to the white lace collar she wore, showing the good, young curve of her small, high breasts. Her legs beneath the full skirt were long and slender and clean-looking, her feet small and shapely in little white moccasins which she wore without socks.

He looked up to find her eyes on him. He flushed hotly, but there was nothing in her face to indicate that she had even noticed his appraisal of her charms. She put a hand on the rock beside her. "Come over here and sit down, Henry; you look tired."

"Bin diggin' 'taters all mornin'," he said self-consciously. "Bertie jist sent me to git some water to warsh with." As he sat down beside her his knuckles brushed her skirt, and at the same time he seemed to smell a fresh sweetness that made his head feel light, from her hair, or her dress, perhaps. Again he felt the strange disturbance inside himself, only this time it wasn't so vague as before. He didn't trust himself to say any more just then, so there was silence between them for a little while.

"Henry." Her tone made it almost a question.

"Yes?"

"School starts next week, Henry. Are you going to go?"

He thought about it a while before he answered, and then it was with another question. "Are you going for sure, Ruth Ann?"

"Yes. Yes, and . . ." she hesitated for a moment, then went on softly, "and Henry, I . . . I want you to—I really do."

He looked at her quickly, but when she met his gaze it was he who blushed and looked away first. He didn't know just what he'd seen in the blueness of her eyes, but it set his blood racing. He mumbled something about having to get back with the water and hurriedly filled the two buckets. He was going to leave without looking at her again, when she touched his arm. Tingling all over, he heard her say, "I really do want you to go, Henry—very much." He stole a quick glance at her, said he'd think about it, and hurried off, sloshing water about his knees.

All the way back home, he hardly noticed the hills or the weight of the buckets, for thinking about what Ruth Ann had said and the way she'd looked at him. He wasn't sure just what it meant, but it was certainly the most exciting thing that had ever happened to him. He could still remember the clean fragrance of her, still feel her hand resting lightly on his arm. He thought that maybe he would go back to school, if she really wanted him to; he knew his father would like it. And he wouldn't have to stay around Bertie all the time.

He quickened his pace, thinking that Bertie would be angry, and that whatever food she had fixed for him would be cold. He squinted up at the sun, saw that it was just past noon. Then he turned the last bend in the road and started up the hill toward the house. As he did, he saw a man come out of the house, get into a car sitting in front, and drive quickly away. There was something familiar about the fellow, but he couldn't be certain from the hurried glimpse he'd had. The car, though, made him pretty sure of the man's identity; it belonged to a fruit-jar salesman who had visited the house several times before. He wondered at his presence now; it certainly wasn't time for Bertie to be buying fruit jars.

Setting down one bucket to open the gate, he picked it up, let the gate swing shut behind him, and went on up to the house. There he found Bertie, flushed and perspiring, just beginning to fix his lunch. Instead of scolding him for taking a long time, she muttered something about his getting back sooner than she'd expected. When she had finished her meager preparations for the meal, she called him into the kitchen to eat. While he was washing his hands, she came up behind him, close, and he could feel her thighs and belly hot against him and her breath on his neck. She said, "You won't say nothin' to nobody about Mr. Travers bein' here, will you, honey?"

He moved away roughly and said between his teeth, "I didn't see nobody, Bertie—nobody at all." She grinned and offered him some warmed-over hoecake.

When the brief meal was over, Henry went out on the front porch and sat there resting for a few minutes, until he heard Bertie coming. Then he got up, put on his old hat, and went back to the potato patch to resume his digging. All afternoon, as he dug, as he pitched the tawny, thin-skinned potatoes into the waiting basket, he could see Ruth Ann's face, with the blue eyes so level and frank. He thought his mother must have looked the same way, at that age. He could hear the soft voice again, "I really do want you to go, Henry—very much."

Suddenly a disturbing thought struck him: Did Bertie know? He quickly dismissed the probability, but remembered the salesman Travers and what Bertie had said to him about keeping Travers's presence a secret. Maybe he knew something on her, instead. He started remembering his first weeks at the house. Travers had come often at first, usually when he was out working in the crops; sometimes he had stayed as much as an hour. Henry stopped digging and stood up straight suddenly, and his shoulders caught him with a sharp pain. And then, in a month or less, Travers had stopped coming, had in fact, not been back until today. The full significance of it hit him all at once, left him feeling weak, almost sick at his stomach.

He decided to quit digging and carried the spading fork and the half-filled basket to the shed. There he sat down in the shade to think about what he was going to do. He wanted to run away for good, but maybe if he started going to school he could stand it, because then he would not be at home very much except when his father was there. He looked at the lengthening shadows about him and judged that his father would be home from work in another hour. He decided to go tell Ruth Ann that he was going to go to school. He though she would be pleased, since she had wanted him to go; and maybe he could talk to her about what he ought to do—about running away or not. He didn't know what a nice girl like her would think about such things, but he felt somehow that she'd understand. Anyway, he wanted to see her again, to find out what, if anything, she'd had in her eyes and her voice for him that morning.

He told Bertie that he didn't want any supper, that he was going to walk down to the store on the highway to see if he could get some shotgun shells. For once, she accepted his statement without comment or question, and he turned to making himself presentable. He washed his face and hands, dusted off his shoes, combed his hair, and rolled down his shirt sleeves. He would have liked to put on a clean shirt and a pair of overall pants, but that would arouse Bertie's suspicions. Finally, he got out the two dollars and ten cents he'd made selling rabbit hides at a dime apiece, just in case Ruth Ann might walk to the store with him for some ice cream or pop.

As he made his way along the winding road between the wooded hills, he relived a dozen times his experience of the morning. He wondered what he'd talk about when he saw Ruth Ann; he'd never had a "date" with a girl, and he didn't know what you were supposed to do. The very thought of going up to Ruth Ann's house, to her parents, and asking for her, made him hesitate and almost turn back. He knew Mr. and Mrs. Higgins, though, and besides, he thought maybe she would be at the spring house, where he could see her by himself. He was almost there now, and he quickened his pace as he reached the top of the last hill. But just before he could see over the crest, he heard voices, a boy and a girl laughing together, and then what he saw stopped him, suddenly shaken out of his dreams, and set him staring.

It was Ruth Ann, gay and laughing as he had seldom seen her, and with her was a boy whom Henry had seen before. They were holding hands. As Henry watched, their arms went around each other's waists. They went out of sight together up the little path that led from the spring house into the woods. They hadn't seen him; he was glad of that, anyway. He couldn't imagine what Ruth Ann was doing with a fellow like Chad Purlow, who cursed and drank and talked dirty about women. He was big and older than either Henry or Ruth Ann; he was darkly handsome and had plenty of money to spend. But Henry just couldn't imagine a nice girl like Ruth Ann having anything to do with Chad Purlow. It just wasn't right for her to do a thing like that.

He knew he had no business prying into their affairs, but he just had to know what Ruth Ann was doing with Chad; he followed the two up the narrow trail between the trees. After a few minutes of rapid, noiseless walking, with the underbrush growing thicker and thicker along the trail, he heard their voices again. Stepping softly now, he peered into a small clearing by the trail—only for a moment; then he turned away and went with swift strides back down the trail.

Coming out on the road, he stood for a long moment looking at the spring house where he had sat that morning with Ruth Ann. He fingered the change in his pocket and set out aimlessly down the dusty, rutted road. The sun had set, and long shadows were beginning to mar the clean outlines of the hills.

Song

Mildred Stites Reed

My mother is a lady
Of pride and cultured air,
But once she was a maiden
With flowers in her hair.

My father is a scholar
With dignity to spare,
But once he touched those curling locks
And kissed the flowers there.

Being Inland

Ethel Davis Ramsay

The lore of lakes is haunting,
The mountain's mystery
Remains alone for wanting
Of souls to set it free,
And rock-cliffs bear upon their breasts
The sea's biography.
But how shall we find wisdom
Who walk a sandy floor,
Who know not lakes nor hills nor cliffs
Nor any windless shore?

Unrest

Ethel Davis Ramsay

Oh, I should be less scornful,
The waiting time less long,
If I could make of fire and wind
Some little song;

And I should quite relinquish
This longing for a flight,
If Ariel would sing to me
Some star-encrusted night.

From a New-Made Grave

Rebecca Kirkpatrick Sprinkle

I wish that I had read that little book.
The yellow of its jacket was so bright
It gleamed from out the crowd of dusty browns
  Like friendly light.

Between those covers must have been encased
A taste of some mad joy or frantic fear;
I might have pondered on its wisdom now.
  How thick the dust is here!

For Jane from Durham

Creighton Gilbert

Every summer of my living I have here returned
From the static piles of the frenzied exhausted city
Or Europe's chapels, where the thing that order designed,
In fading assertion, gave valid cure to the mind.

I come to the holiday of the inert nerve,
To lie in a weedy meadow, swamp after rain,
With tennis court, club house, and cheese-box swimming
pool.
Around me, at each habitual return of the date,
The machinery of laughter is set up: and away its disciples
Whirl on themselves with syncopation of purpose.
"Forest Hills," pretty title, the listless ornament
Dragged from this real-estate culture, whose affable gods
Are lipstick, coke, auto, and body, always dependable
To keep cold off ego and give it luxurious welter.

In the gaiety of noise and bold color, the quick attraction,
The exhibited and hidden bargaining of sex, I flowed
A small intruder, ready to fall in quietly,
Seeking and finding the same remedy as they
For a different trouble—the utter surcease unto death,
All-passive, the least intense of the livable worlds.

Now a new summer begins, I report here to open
The inventory of newest problems and pleasures,
Settling and finding them you, whose mobile image
Pervades the green of the lush weeds and wild onions—
—They are surely Philistines, their arched and careless bodies
Avoiding frightening thought, and best off with a beer—
O bright jewel, in exile illumine the tennis courts!
What would you think, bride, of my habit's old traffics?
Changed, as I rule alone the sudden decay
Where last summer's new playground has never been used,
For the boys now are all in camp among swerving seas,
Or, sunken to Guadalcanal, dream of this ease.

Pale Spring Falls Gently

Olive Sherertz Lanham

Pale spring falls gently on this quiet earth,
That here is yet unmarked by war's rough scars;
The fresh damp smell of rain-soaked grass gives birth
To fragrant hope. But only April stars
And memory, like a brief, gray wisp of wind,
Whisper to you that spring has come—at home.
For seas are blue and hot, and endless din
Of battle stuns the air, and reddened foam
Dries on the alien sand of beaches where
You fight and kill—ten thousand miles away.
Yet . . . we will walk through pools of twilight air
When you return to me some distant day;
The bitterness you feel will fade and cease,
And spring will touch your soul with green, cool peace.

One of the Darkies

Ovid Williams Pierce

ON THAT chilly morning in the fall of the year when one of the darkies rushed into the house and announced to Mister Preston that Matthew was dying, Miss Adelaide was in the room and, of course, heard. Matthew? she repeated to herself as soon as her brother had hurried out. Matthew? Which one of the darkies was he? To save her life she couldn't remember Matthew's face. What a queer feeling this gave her! One of those countless darkies who lived around the plantation was at this moment dying, and she didn't know which it was. Most of the faces she recognized even when she saw them away from the plantation; and at one time or another she had probably heard all the names; but she had not the slightest idea which names belonged to which people. "Matthew, Matthew," she kept on saying, as if to summon his face before her. And, as a matter of fact, many faces did appear, those that she saw every day somewhere about her. But as each hovered there, as though in a cloud before her eyes, each remained obstinately nameless. She was obliged to admit that to her they were all "darkies." She'd taken them as a matter of course, as if they'd always been here and always would be. Even as she'd been aware of the boxwood at the front of the house and the fruit trees at the back, she'd been aware of them as belonging here. But now from this dark, voiceless group one had just stepped forth to attract her attention.

And it was most disturbing to her that she could not remember his face. She could not tell upon which of the many the hand of death had now been placed.

She got up and went over to the back window, from which she could see a great part of the yard and some of the fields where the Negroes worked. Nobody was in sight. And this was strange, for Negroes had been picking cotton all morning in these lower fields. Although the day was chilly, she raised the window about half a foot and stooped as if to communicate with somebody outside. But she heard not a sound. Then a few oak leaves, brown and crisp, made a light scraping sound as the wind hurried them over the hard-packed earth. Miss Adelaide looked toward the woodpile. She remembered that just a short while ago a man had come to split kindling. Now he was gone. His ax lay against the chopping block, its blade shining in the sun. From the woodpile she looked toward the meathouse, the barn. Still not a soul.

A sudden feeling of loneliness came over her. She couldn't remember having felt so much alone in all her life. Everybody had left her to go see this Matthew die. Everybody. All the darkies, and even Preston; something had drawn them from the fields, the barns, the firesides, had drawn them all but her. She alone remained. That which drew the others seemed not to touch her. She was outside.

What was she doing on this plantation, anyway? How had it come about that she was living here among these strange people—among these darkies whose names she did not even know? For a second these questions made her feel dizzy, as if fact and fancy had suddenly become indistinguishable. Preston? He was real, of course. He was her brother. But what did she know of him? Not much more than she knew of the others, the strange ones outside.

Frightened, Miss Adelaide drew back from the window, wishing somebody would appear. Had the cook left the kitchen? she wondered.

Keeping very still in her chair in front of the fire, she tried to make her thoughts lie quietly. How she wanted to get back the state of mind she'd been in before the darky came! But it wouldn't come back. The uncomfortable feeling lay somewhere deep within her that she had an issue to meet before she could rest again. She had a matter to explain to herself, and there was to be no quiet until she did so.

Was it right that a person should know so little of others? For a whole year now she'd been living here. She'd come to take the place of her brother's wife. What a sorry job of it she must have made! Yet it hadn't been expected of her that she could fill such a place. One who had traveled the world, lived in hotels, who'd had none to seek, none to leave—how could such a one take the place of her brother's wife? What preparation had she for life among Negroes? And yet Miss Adelaide would always remember the pleasure that her brother's letter had given her—the letter asking her to come here to keep him company if she'd become tired of hotels and traveling and if she wasn't afraid she'd get homesick at night when she had only crickets and frogs to listen to. He'd added that she'd be a comfort to him. And it was this that had touched her as few things ever had. Perhaps because it was the last thing she'd expected him to say. It had given her a strange sensation. She'd thought the time long past when anybody could want her.

Well, in the year that had gone by since then, had she been a comfort? She couldn't tell. She had no way of knowing. But if she hadn't been, it was because she hadn't known how. On the other hand, just to herself, she could say that the year had been something of a disappointment to her. Preston hadn't been the man she'd expected to find, not the brother she'd known. He'd given her the feeling that he hadn't called her to watch him live, but to watch him die. She'd soon found that his living had already been done, with somebody else. But she did believe that if Preston had ever reminded her it was another's place she held, he'd done so unintentionally. "Tempe," Miss Adelaide murmured. Another stranger. This furniture about her had been collected by Tempe. All this had been hers.

Yes, and for forty years her brother had slept with this strange woman. What could she possibly know of this closed world they'd made between them? Putting Preston in bed with Tempe made him seem all the more strange to her, impressed upon her with a chilling sensation how little she herself was able to touch him. Truly, his life had been spent. This was only a period of waiting—until his time came to follow. Wasn't it a little selfish of him to ask her to watch? But thoughts like these got Miss Adelaide nowhere, and she tried not to think them. After all, perhaps she was as well off here as anywhere. She wasn't even sure where she'd go if she left. Back to her travels? What did she call home? Ships? Yes, ships . . . as much as any place. She could truthfully say that the ocean she dearly loved; it had been for her a great source of happiness. A little tinge of warmth and excitement came to her when she thought of returning, of leaving this cold, hostile place —this great shell of a house wherein two other people had already lived out their lives.

She drew her chair a little closer to the fire. No wonder she hadn't known the poor dying darky; no wonder he was just one of many. If her brother had become a stranger, it was hardly probable that she'd know one of the others. For the Negroes weren't even supposed to enter her world. They were the background folk, the unknown who worked below, who behind the scenes kept things going.

And what a lot of servants she'd had in her lifetime! Bellboys, clerks, maids, nurses, stewards, waiters—all to be had for a price, all where one needed them. No, she didn't know much about them, either. And many a one had served her in his time, too! But she'd paid them all well. Yet there'd been something about paying them that had kept her from getting close to them. There'd never seemed to be a need for warmth. Actually the times had been few when money hadn't been enough. Indeed, hadn't she often stood in mortal fear of the day she'd lose that money?

Suddenly, then, she was seized by an alarming thought. This unknown Matthew who now lay dying was not only Matthew, but the countless others as well, the dead and forgotten, who had walked with and served her in the past. Secure with her money, she'd let life slip by without trying to grasp, without even knowing the need for grasping. And now at her feet another lay dying—one who would remain unknown to her forever.

Miss Adelaide stopped rocking. She was almost overcome by a feeling of futility. She felt helpless and old. How many times hadn't she told herself before that people were happier when they stopped trying!

Surrendering as she had not in a long time to a nameless but almost restful despair, she sat for a great while, not bothering to move except to dab at her eyes and to twist absently the tiny bit of handkerchief she held. Was it too late for her to join the others? she wondered. Would they mind if she came to see Matthew dying? Was it too late for her to know something of this stranger who was passing?

These questions aroused in her a surprising little quiver of hope. She could find out, surely. Amazed by her own sudden boldness, Miss Adelaide took her shawl and went into the yard. She felt as if she were about to make an exciting experiment. Where did Matthew live? She didn't know. But she could tell . . . it would be where the crowd had gathered. She couldn't possibly miss them, for there would be a great number. They who were not strangers to one another, they who belonged here on this plantation, would be together.

The fresh, cold air almost took her breath. It was much colder outside than she'd thought. Earlier, as she'd watched the Negroes from her window, she hadn't dreamed it was this cold. The Negroes certainly hadn't shown it; they'd looked comfortable to her. It startled one sometimes to think what they had to put up with. She tightened her shawl about her neck.

Had Matthew been a cotton-picker? she wondered. She looked around at the far-reaching fields, where shortly before men and women had been working. Not a living soul was in sight. Piles of cotton had been left on the sheets at the edges of the fields. Work had been stopped suddenly.

This feeling of being left she didn't like; though different, she believed it worse in the open than in the house. Was Matthew such a beloved one among them that nothing could go on? Even the cook had left the kitchen.

As she approached the gate a bird dog, seeing that she was going through, ran up behind her, was at her heels before she knew it. Her heart jumped and a flush of warmth rose to her cheeks. But when her fright passed she felt ashamed. Certainly there was no need for this! As though to reassure herself that she and the dog understood each other, she leaned over and tried to pat him. But the dog was impatient. He ran forward and leaped up at the gate, showing clearly he had no time for play. Unmistakably rebuked, Miss Adelaide began to pull upon the heavy gate. Into the narrowest crack that would admit his body the dog forced himself; then, free, he bounded off across the field as if he'd long been separated from his pack and had just found the trail. Miss Adelaide, with that empty feeling people have when suddenly abandoned, for a moment did not move. She felt more strangely alone than ever. Even the dog was leaving her outside, answering to something the other strangers round her had answered to. Was it possible that he could be looking for Matthew? Perhaps, even, he was Matthew's dog.

A little farther down the sandy road which now lay sunken and narrow between the heavy, full growth upon the fields, she stopped to rest for a moment and to look about. The exercise had caused her breath to come fast, but the cool October air against her face gave her skin a pleasant tingle. Absently as she stood there she began to pull a stringy fluff of cotton which had burst from its hard brown boll. Then, without thinking, she pulled another and another, reaching each time for a lower boll upon the stalk. In a moment both her hands were full, and she couldn't tell that the stalk had been touched. With a little lift of excitement she decided that she could finish one stalk at least. Of all the thousands and thousands around her! She bent over now and started to work in earnest. Surely she could clean one stalk! But the strain of bending over was too great, and the bolls grew too low. For this kind of work she needed a chair. Smiling feebly at the pitiful little pile she'd picked, she shook her head. And *they* picked all day long! What a great part of his life Matthew must have spent here! How did the darkies stand this back-breaking work? As she looked about at the veritable sea of cotton around her, she was almost overwhelmed. It all had to be picked, boll by boll. And darkies had been doing it for more than a hundred years. Yes, and in his own lifetime, for bread and meat, Matthew had done his share. He'd started as a child and he'd stopped—this morning. He and the nameless others, the dead no less nameless than the living. What a shocking thought! One boll at a time, over acres and acres. This was more than Miss Adelaide could take in. Ten hours a day. Six days a week. Plowing, planting, picking. Here, before she was born, the long dead and the unknown had worked, under this same sun, within sight of these trees. Now another who had labored here was leaving to join the old and forgotten ones.

Beyond the cotton field, Miss Adelaide stopped at the fence which enclosed the stable lot. The mules were all inside, standing about as if it were Sunday. Some were drinking from a long trough; others were feeding. Miss Adelaide looked at the two or three nearest her. They seemed singularly indifferent to the presence of one so strange, for they slowly turned away from her to drink and feed with the others. One of these mules Matthew had plowed. Did mules know people? she wondered. Would one of these strange beasts ever notice that Matthew had gone? A sudden curiosity seized her. She wished she had somebody to ask: she wanted to know which of these mules Matthew had plowed. She felt that if she could determine this she'd have something definite about him to remember. With her forehead wrinkled and her eyes narrowed against the sun, she looked intently from one mule to another. It was no use. They were all alike. Then, suddenly, there before her eyes, one mule stepped forth from the others. Miss Adelaide could hardly believe what she was seeing. Matthew's mule had come forward. She knew it was Matthew's. She was aware of a quickening of her heartbeat. Powers she knew nothing of had allowed her to see him.

This was as far as Miss Adelaide had ever walked from the house. If she didn't hurry back now her lunch would be ready, and nobody would know where to find her. It didn't matter if others were late, but she knew that her absence would cause alarm. How like a child she'd been treated.

Then she remembered. Her lunch wasn't ready. Nobody was at home. The cook had left more than an hour ago. What a strange, unnatural day! She wasn't even to have her meals on time. Such a queer day as this she couldn't recall having seen before. Everybody had run off and left her to wander about this great plantation; no lunch was being prepared for her; and here she was looking at mules in the stable lot. Yes, she and the animals had the plantation to themselves.

Which way had she better look now to find the others? She hadn't the slightest idea. But since she'd come so far, a little farther wouldn't matter. She certainly had no reason to go home.

Slowly she started around the lot, taking the narrow footpath which ran by the fence. At the corner of the lot she turned and came to an abrupt stop. For, across the field, stood the cabin in which Matthew lay dying.

The yard was packed with the darkies; they'd even crowded the porch and were looking in the windows and the door. Somewhere inside, close to the bed perhaps, was her brother Preston, the doctor for all.

Coming upon the house so unexpectedly, Miss Adelaide had been given a little shock; inside her she could feel her heart beating very fast. Here were the people who had left her. She hadn't been frightened, but she was glad that the last hour was over. Looking back upon it, she didn't mind admitting now that it hadn't been pleasant. With a brisker step and a lighter heart, she hurried on.

But the darkies round the cabin remained motionless. They had their backs to her. For a moment, as she watched this crowd of silent people, it seemed to her that she was looking at a great mural, but a truly wonderful one upon which the figures are about to move and from which voices are about to rise. In the background of the painting, as far as she could see, stretched the dark green of the pine forest; closer, to the right and left, lay the proud fields, swollen with a snowy whiteness; and in the center, under the towering oaks which shaded the yard and kept it grassless, stood the cabin. Everywhere around it the motionless figures were waiting.

So intent, so eager were they to hear from within that they did not see her coming. There was not a sign that they knew she was near.

Truly, she told herself, they did not need her now. This was not the time to go among them. Miss Adelaide stopped. But she'd wanted so badly to—What?

At that second, just as she put the question to herself, she heard a muffled cry rise from the crowd. Like a single bird suddenly released, it hung above the yard and was gone. The figures which had been painted now came to life. A wave of movement passed through them. They pressed closer to the door from which word had come.

Matthew was dead.

Miss Adelaide felt a sudden tightness in her throat. Then she was aware of a feeling of emptiness. There was no need to go farther. She was too late. It was as if the goal toward which she'd set her feet had suddenly disappeared from the horizon, leaving nothing but unbelievable space ahead.

Yes, he was dead. There was no need for her to go on. This Matthew she could never know. She had seen his mule, his cotton field, his dog. But she was not to see him. She was too late. He could never be more than one of the darkies. He was to remain unknown to her forever.

Slowly Miss Adelaide turned. Now surely it was time to go home.

Winter Sunset: 1941

John Schaffner

Now the red sun goes down into the mountains,
Leaving us without light in our troubled lands.
There are flames in the sky but they have no warmth for us
Who stand here alone in the night with empty hands.

We stand here waiting for the new tomorrow
And a new sun to make of this a greener earth.
Then little streams will thaw, there will be planting.
Now in the winter we should prepare for birth.

Now in the winter we will grow strong and rocklike,
And if the sun is late in its coming back
We will be marble, we will be granite, standing.
In a new ice age we'll not be the ones to crack.

Now that the sun has gone down behind the mountains
We stand alone against the empty sky
Like a few brief monuments to the first who dared
Face out the night after watching the last god die.

On Southern Station

John Schaffner

Past the pale small stars, to the north
we see the shadow fly.
Like a moth, like a rigid bird
the plane cuts the southern sky
bisecting the heavenly arc.
Then the eastbound plane in flight
at a right angle makes into the dark
and lays an invisible cross on the night
star-flowered and blue.
Here also our crossroads are
where the heart's way—northward to you—
is crossed by the dark path of war.

Poem: 1944

John Schaffner

Whether asleep or dead or merely drunk with wine—
leave him alone. Let him have his dream.
For the moment he is free. He has gone home.

Beside whatever hedge, or ditch, or strange polluted stream
his body sprawls, let it have peace
that the heart may seek out its own kingdom.

The fields were never half so bright where he came from
as now these aching miles and thousand lives away
when he revisits them all clad in glory.

The guns are still, the helmet forgotten on the head—
see him there, lying in moon-broken shade:
let nothing disturb the sleeping warrior's bed.

The Wolf Fenris

Henry A. Simons

GEORGE GREEN finished his typing with a final burst of speed, jerked the long sheet of copy paper out of the typewriter, and dropped it on top of the other sheets on the side of the desk. He then picked up the whole pile, bounced its edges on the desk to align them, and began to make little rapid marks on the sheets with his blue pencil. His bony fingers held the pencil tightly and darted out again and again to dig savagely into the paper when some correction was indicated. He wrote a large "30" at the end of the story and ruffled back to the first sheet. Quickly he sketched in a headline, counted it with the little bird-like hops of his pencil point, and scribbled "18 point, 3 lines" beside it. Then he sighed deeply, dropped the pencil, and slumped back in his chair. George Green was tired.

"Pretty tired," he said. His words were startling in the empty newspaper office. He stood up and snapped off the green, cone-shaped lamp that swung from the ceiling over his desk. Walking around the four other silent and deserted desks that filled the office, he came to the coat rack that stood in the corner. First he carefully put on his gray felt hat, and then after rolling down his sleeves he took his coat from the hook, slung it over his arm, and walked out of the office. "Just time for a beer at Turner's," he said, looking at his pocket watch. He walked down the steps of the two-story building of the Centerville *News* and strode out into the Ohio summer night.

He was not a conspicuous man. In any crowd he went unnoticed, remembered only as a fairly tall, stoop-shouldered person who wore a gray suit and an old gray hat. His face was long and sad; his hair, straight and brown. Twenty-eight of his forty-six years he had worked for the Centerville *News,* first as a reporter and then as rewrite man, the position he now held.

George Green stepped out into the sad light of summer evening and stood for a moment in the street, looking like some voyager from a far-off land who had just walked into the edge of the town and surveyed the buildings with a quiet calm of one who has come among strangers many times and not yet found a home. For a moment he stood wrapped in the dying light of evening, and then he turned and walked along the street toward the center of town and Turner's saloon. As he walked, the air came to life with the scents blown off the fields at the edge of town—scents of ripening grain and rich black soil.

And then from far away to the north of Centerville came the rising rumble of the heavy freight train that passed the town every night at the same time. Green slowed his walk and listened. The warm summer air, the dying light, and the rumble of the faraway train struck him suddenly with the vivid memory of a time long ago when as a small boy of six he had heard that same sound coming from the north. He remembered standing in the study his father had used before his death, looking up at the great shelves with their row on row of books. It was the only thing his father had left them, those great rows of books. He remembered how in later life he had read in those books, coming frequently upon some faded annotation in the margin; and though he had never known his father, the man seemed to be in the room with him then, and he would say to himself, "He was a great man."

But as a boy of six he had taken particular delight in one volume. It was a large faded book of Norse fables, covered in brown calfskin, with gilded pages and large engravings of gods and goddesses. Odin was there, and Heimdall, keeper of the Bridge of Bifröst, and Freya the fair goddess of love, and the great wolf Fenris. The great wolf Fenris.

"Read me about Fenris, Mom. Read about Fenris," he would beg, sometimes bringing her the great book, which almost weighed him down.

His mother would laugh and run her fingers through the soft brown hair that always fell over his forehead and say to him, "But George, we've read that one at least a dozen times. Don't you ever get tired of it?"

"Read me about Fenris. Please," he would repeat, pleading with a dignity that always touched her heart.

So she would take the great book from him and open it on her lap. While he sat on the floor with his knees pulled up under his chin, she would read again the story of the great wolf Fenris that was the child of Loki, of how the gods of Valhalla tried vainly to chain him and of how

Fenris always broke away, until finally they bound him forever, not with chains, but with threads of magic too thin to break.

In his child's mind George built a fantasy around the wolf. He dreamed that Fenris was there with him, there in his Ohio home, and that together the two of them would go out through the back door of the house, past the woodpile and the dilapidated chicken house until they came to the long dirt lane that ran away between the farms and woods of Centerville. There he would climb onto the broad back of the great wolf and slap his rump; and with a great leap they would be off, running swiftly and easily over the hard-packed earth of the lane, through the fields of greening wheat and oats, across the lonely asphalt highway that wound out of the distance and ran through Centerville to disappear into the distance again. They would run hard and free, the great wolf with his head down and his ears pressed tight against his majestic head, until they had left behind the last trace of humanity, until they came to a shallow creek bounded by willows, and here he would dismount and silently wait while Fenris drank in the creek. Then, together, they would walk back to the town, he with his arm over the great gray shoulder of the wolf, until they came again to his house.

Once he had told his mother about his fantasy, and she had treated him like a child. "Of course it's not just a dream, dear," she had said. "He's just as real as you are. Listen! There, you can hear his howling, can't you?" He stood there in the study with her and listened to the rumble of the freight train that passed to the north of Centerville every evening. Then he looked at her for a moment and turned and left the room. He never talked about it again.

But now as George Green stood in the street in front of the Centerville *News* building and listened to the rattling train pass in the night, his mother's foolish metaphor came back to him and brought with it words of long ago and the half-forgotten child's fantasy of Fenris the wolf.

He stood for a moment longer and then continued on his way to Turner's saloon and his nightly glass of beer.

George Green shifted his coat from his right arm to his left and pushed open the door of Joe Turner's saloon.

"Hello, Joe," he said as he stepped into the cool room and up to the bar.

"Evenin', George." The bartender paused in his task of wiping the bar to look up and ask, "Draft?"

"Yeah, a tall one."

"Anything new in town?" asked the bartender as he directed the jet of amber beer against the sides of a glass he was rotating with practiced dexterity.

"Not a damn thing." George Green took the beer and watched the head slowly rise and overflow the sides of the glass. "One wedding—the Jennings girl, you know—and old man Crowley's auctioning off his two work horses Saturday. That's about all."

For a while he drank his beer and watched the lazy turning of the big, broad-bladed electric fan overhead. Then the bartender spoke again.

"Done any more writin' on that book of yours?"

Green laughed, "No. Haven't found any time for it. I'll get to it sometime soon, though."

He thought: Sometime soon. My God, I'm forty-six and my novel's still in my desk, just the first chapter. My time's running out—is it forty-six years already?—and it's still just the first chapter. If I died tonight, how long would I be remembered? A year? Maybe. Maybe.

"Yeah, I know how it is. Never seem to get to do what you want to. No time, I guess." The bartender paused in his cleaning and wiping and leaned over the bar. "You know, I always wanted to do some trapping myself. Don't get the time though. There's lots of muskrats down in Beaver Creek. Good hides bring a buck and a quarter in Columbus. Just the other day I was talking to old man Summers about some traps. . . ."

George Green stopped listening. Old man Summers, he thought, Jim Summers and Frances. Frances. He repeated the name over again to himself. Once again—as it always had in the past—that name opened up the floodgates of forgotten memory, and the day brightened, yet saddened intolerably at the same time.

Like almost all men, he had been in love when he was young. He had loved as only a young man can love for the first time—with all the intense strength of his April days, his wild joys and endless dreams. Old men look back on the time of first love, and, remembering, they write of armored knights and troubadors, of fairies and the lands where life is somehow better than it is here. And when that first love has passed something goes out of the boy forever, and he is then a man, remembering from time to time and knowing that there was once an hour when he was finer than other men and that the hour can never come again.

So now he remembered. He remembered how he had gone down to Lester's Livery stable on the edge of town to hire a carriage for his first big date with Frances. He had appraised the horses slowly, occasionally muttering to himself, trying to give the impression that he was an old judge of horses. Old Jeff Lester, bent and worn, watched with his watery eyes of pale blue, chuckled and said, "Big date, huh, son?"

"That's right," he had replied. "Nothing but the best for this one."

Old Jeff Lester had winked and chuckled and finally hitched up a chestnut mare to the carriage. "Now there you are, son. She's a spirited one, so hold her in."

Then George Green had taken the reins and driven away from the stable with its warm smells of hay and leather, driven down through town past the court house and the new brick school until he came to her house—Frances' house. When they drove together back through the town, he sat upright, looking very proud as he passed the town people. Occasionally he looked over at the slim young girl beside him, at her bronze, sun-filled hair, and her deep brown eyes.

On the outskirts of town he had pulled up beside a grove of trees and unhitched the horse. Then they walked slowly through the trees to a spot where the grass grew tall and green. George and Frances walked hand in hand to the shadow of a large elm and sat down. And there he talked—shyly at first— but with growing confidence while the sun went down and the chestnut mare grazed and snorted in the tall grass.

"I want to write," he had said. "More than anything else in the world, I want to write. Great words." He ran his fingers through the soft brown hair that fell over his forehead. "Simple words are best. If I could just learn to put simple words together so they said great things. Like

Lincoln did. You know what I mean." He threw himself backwards on the ground in his exasperation at not being able to express himself to her.

"You will," she had laughed. "You'll write a book some day and be famous and everybody in Centerville will say, 'There goes George Green, the famous author.' " Her eyes glowed as she thought of herself as the wife of the richest man in town, and living in the biggest house, bigger even than the white house on the hill that belonged to banker Caldwell.

"What will you write? Love stories?"

"No. Maybe I'll write about dreams. What they're all about, I mean. I had a dream once when I was a kid, and I've always wondered about it." He glanced at her, somewhat embarrassed at what he was saying. "It was about a wolf named Fenris who used to come to my house, and we'd go outside together, and he would carry me on his back until he was tired. Then we'd come back to the house."

"Is that all?" she asked, puzzled.

"Yes. What do you suppose it meant?"

"Nothing. That's just silly." She laughed quickly and stood up.

A sudden gust of wind blew her broad-brimmed picture hat off and sent it rolling over the ground at a furious rate. With wild shouts of gleeful terror, they chased it. George recovered it in a wheat field near by. When Frances panted to a stop beside him, he put the hat on the back of her disheveled head and took her in his arms. She didn't resist when he kissed her. For a moment they stood waist deep in growing wheat, the grain waving gently about them like the golden minutes of their lives.

George Green stood quietly under the slowly turning fans in Joe Turner's barroom, remembering it all as if it had happened yesterday.

"Good night, Joe," he said to the bartender, "I'll see you tomorrow." He stepped out into the street again.

So what did it all come to? he thought. I went away to school, and she married Jim Summers while I was off learning to say great things with simple words. And what have I said? Countless, yes, innumerable words concerning fires and deaths and marriages—the Jennings girl, you know—and many words also about the two draft horses that old man Crowley is auctioning off this Saturday. Also one chapter of a novel which is still in my desk. Someday I'll find time to work on it, maybe. But if I died tonight? My God, once I had all the strength for it, but it's gone now. What are the chains that they bind us with?

He walked along through the darkening streets towards his home. He seemed unable to forget the girl that had filled his thoughts a few moments before.

"I will go to see her," he said aloud, struck by the idea. "If I can only stand beside her once more—even if she doesn't suspect—it will all be the same as it was in the wheat field. Even the golden grain will come back again. All the magic, the vanished years, the strength—she could snap the chain if I could only stand beside her again."

For a moment he stood indecisively looking down a side street. Then he turned down it, passed under the street-light, and started walking towards Frances Summers' house.

The Summers house was set back from the street. A white fence about waist high enclosed the well-kept lawn which ran up to a bed of flowers beside the veranda of the house. George Green pushed open the gate and walked up to the veranda steps and rang the door bell. In a minute a woman came through the hall, peered out between the curtains, and then opened the door.

"Hello, Frances."

"Why, George," the woman said. "Come in. Jim isn't here right now, but he'll be back in a little while. He's taking Johnny down to buy a pair of shoes. Boys are so hard on shoes, but you just can't do a thing with them. Come in and sit down."

And George Green, once he had stepped inside the house, suddenly felt very foolish. He looked at the woman before him as though she were some stranger. She was his own age, a large, stout woman in a cotton house-dress. Her face was heavily powdered, and her hair was covered with a net that protected the artificial wave. She led him into the living room, and he sat down beside her on the couch. He felt the need of saying something.

"Well, how's everything with you?"

"Everything's fine. Jim's expanding the business, you know. He's bought out the store next to ours, and we're going to remodel the places into one big store."

"That's good. Jim's getting to be a big man in Centerville. I guess you can be proud of him."

"Yes, I guess I can. How about you, George? Have you done any more work on your novel?" she asked.

"No. I haven't had time." He stood up and turned away from her. Slowly and deliberately he answered. "That's not quite true. I've had the time, but I haven't got anything inside me. I'm just a small-town newspaperman that wanted to write. That's all. Once maybe I had something, but it's gone now. I'm like that wolf—I told you about that but you wouldn't remember—I ran free and strong once, but they've bound me with threads too thin to break. God, how can they bind us with threads?" His voice trembled; he still faced away from her, looking out of the window. His knuckles showed white as he clenched his hands behind his back.

"I'm sorry," he said slowly, "I'm sorry. It's just that I'm upset. I worked too late tonight."

"Of course," she said. "And don't worry; you'll finish that book someday soon. I always said you'd be a great writer."

He smiled. "I'd better be going, now."

"Yes, I guess you had better go."

She led him out of the living room to the front door and then walked with him down the walk to the white gate that opened on the road. She said goodbye to him and watched him walk off until the gathering night had almost swallowed him up.

And then as Frances Summers stood by the gate, she might have seen, if she had had eyes, a shadow, a great animal shape walking along beside George Green, who was resting his hand on the head of the pacing beast. Then suddenly, as though the man had given some signal, she might have seen the shadowy shape leap forward and run strong and free up the rising grade of the road. As the shadow passed under the street light, she might have seen that it was a huge gray wolf, running like a wraith, its great head down and its ears pressed tightly back. Swift and hard it raced over the hard-packed earth of the road, finally cutting to the left and continuing its run through the fields of greening wheat and oats, across the lonely asphalt highway that wound out of the distance, on and on, never halting in its unhurried pace until it reached the horizon, where a ladder of stars dipped down to earth, and without breaking stride the great gray form passed effortlessly up through the night until it got a firm footing on the white road of the Milky Way, and even as she listened, Frances Summers might have heard its measured footfalls die away in the distance.

When she looked back at the road, all she saw was the figure of a man walking slowly out of the light of the street lamp.

Reflections on Reading a Sonnet by William Shakespeare

Kenneth Dougal McDougall

So long as men can breathe or eyes can see,
So long lives this, and this gives life to thee.

O poet who in other days
Wrote those immortal words of praise,
You little guessed but I can see
You penned indeed a prophecy.

My breath is warm, my eyes are clear,
And I behold your lady dear.
More temperate than a summer's day,
She still outlives the mortal clay.

For nature's course has not untrimmed
Nor yet have change or ages dimmed
Those features that you loved so well
And strove in singing words to tell.

I also love, I also hear
Death's winged chariot drawing near.
I too my love in song would save
From the chill fingers of the grave.

But, oh, alas! I lack your power
To lengthen out love's little hour.
Dead poet! Teach me how to sing
Such happy songs that tears shall spring

To the bright eyes of other men!
That day will seem less bitter then
When Time and Death shall wrench apart
Her beauty and my loving heart.

["Somewhere in North Africa," November, 1943]

Gray Street

Opal Winstead

Along that gray and crooked street
One early learns to be discreet.

Old Jordan brought her from the hills.
His wife had died six months before;
And, tired from working in the mills,
He needed her to sweep the floor
And sew dark buttons on his shirt,
And cook his meals and chase the dirt.

I wondered what had made her come
From quiet lands beneath the stars
To this—thick smoke, the looms' low hum.
She said, "To ride the trolley cars,
And wear fine clothes and see the sights,
The buildings and the blazin' lights."

He taught her that "a woman's place"
Is not "a-gaddin' on the street,

A-fingerin' some silk or lace,
Or at the show where people meet
To nod and talk and smile and preen
At silly pictures on a screen."

Then later, venturing forth but at night,
She'd loose her ragged, cotton blouse,
And stand and bathe her face in light
Which offered memories to rouse
Her soul, as solace for the wrong
Of grimy hands that stopped the song.

Nobody knew just how she died.
Old Jordan was a bit upset,
And peevish too, it seemed. I cried
On looking at her face. And yet

Along that gray and crooked street
One early learns to be discreet.

To a Sundial near the Sea

Harold Grier McCurdy

Mute critic of stretched sails and screaming gulls,
sun's monument and shadow's, silent clock,
opposing to the flight of wings and hulls
the slow defiance of impassive rock,
with stiff uplifted finger of hard bronze
precisely cleaving hour from brief hour,
Timevoyager, for whom the seas are ponds,
and vast seawinds the breathing of a flower:
We men, we seagulls, vagrants, restless voices,
screaming against the wind, the spray, the night,
we slender keels gulfed in the great seanoises,
whose only strength is in quick cunning flight:
We, wheeling round you, tranced and heavyeyed,
weave helpless garlands for your granite pride.

Our Little Trains

Archie Robertson

THOUGH many little jerkwater railroad lines have been cruelly torn up for scrap in the past few years, they remain a part of America's uncollected folklore. Perhaps only a third of some four hundred surviving short lines still offer passenger service. But all states save three have *some* surviving dinkies. Arkansas, the state most famed in slow-train literature, still boasts nine; Texas has fourteen; and the top rank is held by the patriotic people of Georgia, with nineteen.

In their old age these lines resort to all sorts of stratagems to survive; Model T's cut down to run on the rails are not uncommon. They will do almost anything to oblige. A Florida short line helped out the local farmers one year when the tomatoes ripened late, after the cannery had closed down. The trusty old steam engine pulled up on the cannery siding and preserved the crop very handily with steam from its boiler. Perhaps the most earnest effort to pay its way was made by the Rutland, Toluca & Northern, in Illinois. In one last effort to satisfy its creditors, a grand public wreck was advertised and a crowd gathered in a cornfield to watch Engines 50 and 51 crash head-on at full speed.

On a spring day it brings a feeling of joy and relaxation to board the Blueberry Express at Concord, New Hampshire, as it puffs tranquilly on a siding with its lone passenger-baggage coach trailing a string of boxcars.

After we get underway the conductor opens the door of the baggage-compartment and the men gather around the stove to smoke, watching the country rock by the open door, close and companionable; a woman hanging up the wash by a stone springhouse waves at the train, her mouth full of pins; the peep-peep of baby chicks traveling by express mingles with the creaking of the droopy wooden car. After the Suncook Valley cuts off its last boxcar of fertilizer at the Farmers' Exchange, the train turns itself around on a wye track, and we jog along with just the engine in front of us, the heaving shoulders of the fireman plainly visible. "It seems almost like the first train," says the tourist across the aisle.

The signs and portents of the true Slow Train are hard to classify. It may be the lady who asks the conductor, as we follow a twisting creek, if she can have a fishing line, or her little girl at whom the conductor stares long and hard; she certainly *looks* more than twelve, but there is nothing he can do about it. Or in the smoking-compartment, as the local chuffs and shudders with stupendous effort as it climbs a grade, a fellow-passenger is almost sure to say, "First-class passengers, keep your seats; second-class passengers, get out and walk; third-class passengers, get out and push." This is from the paper-bound work which all the train butchers used to sell, and which is still found at an occasional way station, *On a Slow Train Through Arkansas,* by Thomas W. Jackson. For the better part of a century, slow trains and the drummers who rode them were a fountainhead of national humor, which dried up only after the drummers took to the highroads and people began to smoke and tell dirty jokes in all parts of the train.

There is no telling how many slow-train addicts there are, but their number must be fairly large. The fans collect everything—old trolley and train tickets, transfers, flagstaffs, tokens, expired passes, sections of old rail, timetables of deceased railroads, no-good bond and stock issues, oil cans, dining-car menus, blotters, paper currency which railroads issued in the old days, rulebooks, anything else which can be moved.

Our motives, to the layman, may perhaps seem obscure, but it should be made clear that the admirers of slow trains do not ride them, or write about them, to make fun of their obsolete equipment and generally old-fashioned ways. Any operating railroad is a living thing and not a curio. Its financial and personal roots go deep into local history and pride. The smaller the railroad, the more important it seems as an institution. Sentiment and dollars get all scrambled up in a most delightful way, and it is for the spiritual qualities they represent that many small trains are passionately defended when their abandonment is proposed.

In the spring of 1940, when high water washed out part of the line of the narrow-gauge East Tennessee & Western North Carolina, more generally known, on account of its diminutive whistle, as Tweetsie, I felt as if an old friend had suffered a mortal stroke. I used to teach school near Tweetsie's line and occasionally rode her to the movies at the county seat. For the people in the mountains she was a reminder of the days when men came seeking the timber on the hillsides and the wealth in the mines, before the first farm family from the Blue Ridge went begging for work in the orchards of California.

The owners petitioned to abandon, and the Interstate Commerce Commission held the usual public hearings, at Johnson City, Tenn. Afterwards I read with sad concern the transcript of the testimony. Tucked in the back was a protest which Annette Vance, of Minneapolis, N. C. (population 53), had sent to the ICC examiner in charge of the case. Not knowing quite what to do with it during the hearings—it was in verse form—he had placed it later in the official docket:

> In Carolina how it did rain
> It took from us a little train.
> So long it seems since we heard her blow
> I wonder why it could thus be so.
> Our Tweetsie whom we loved so dear,
> Her coming and going we have ceased to hear.
> The waters rose and took her track,
> We want our little Tweetsie back.
> When she passed we stood amazed,
> We admired her so, we stood and gazed.
> Our memory of her is clear and plain—
> Please send us back our little train.

Red Coat Day

R. P. Harriss

IT WAS about an hour after daybreak, and the jaybirds were still making a raucous how-d'ye-do among the trees of the Grove, where squirrel nests hung loosely in the boughs. An old bo-squirrel darted out of a hollow and ran along a limb above the House, chased by three scolding jays, to plump down on the marquee, its paws scraping on the blackened tin. The squirrel sat with twitching tail for an instant and scrambled away again at the sound of voices below and the opening of a door. A tall man in plain riding habit walked into the yard, followed by a boy.

"You tell Giles to watch the road?"

"Yes, Father, I told him and he sent Pappy Gola."

Man and boy started down the tree-bordered drive toward the highway. From behind the House, and some distance away, came the mellow notes of kenneled hounds, speaking intermittently.

"Old Bluebell," said the man, without shifting his gaze.

"Burly, too," said the staring boy. Then, with animation, "Ain't that a truck? Yep, that's it, all right. I'll go." And as he hurried away the elaborately grotesque figure of an old Negro appeared at the end of the drive, motioning with a stick toward the House. Then came a horseman in a red coat, riding a blaze-faced bay, dazzlingly gay in the October sunshine.

A horse van moved slowly on the uneven road, followed by a van in which rode twenty couples of hounds. More horsemen followed. The horse vans stopped and unloaded by the side of the highway, but the hound van was kept closed. It was large and roomy, with straw bedding on the floor. The boy observed that a rubber hose was attached to the exhaust pipe at the rear, carrying the carbonic fumes up over the roof and away from the supersensitive hound noses. A huntsman in top-boots, white breeches, red coat, black velvet cap, mounted on a bright chestnut horse, came up beside the van, accompanied by three scarlet-coated horsemen on grays. A rider of one of the grays took a little brass hunting horn out of his coat and blew a few short notes. *A-eu! a-eu! eu-eu-eu!* Dully from within the hound van came an answering clamor. The other riders dismounted and swung down the door, and the pack tumbled out, massing in the road with waving sterns.

The plain-note of the horn carried along the drive to listeners at the House. A little later, the thud and scrabble of hooves and the *pad-scrit! pad-scrit!* of dogs' feet on gravel. The horseman who had come out of the House was now in the saddle and waiting on the lawn, with several long-eared plantation hounds clustered about his horse's heels. (There were Bluebell and Burly; Drummer—old

Drum, whose voice was like the plucked strings of a bass fiddle; Rouster, the quarrelsome; Sheriff, Bugler, Fifer, Bounce, Nimble, and Witchcraft.) When the first red-coated rider reached the House, the two horsemen nodded and then rode off together, disappearing into a thicket.

When they were gone the riders on the grays reached the House, bringing up the guest pack. Hounds seemed to flow over the lawn in rolling waves of color: black backs, white chests, white feet, tan ears, tan markings. The horseman on the blaze-faced bay made little caressing sounds, audible whispers, chirrupings, mimicry of the horn notes. He told over their names, softly, for their names were autumnal melody. (Ringwood, Dashwood, Robin, Patrona, Pirate, Gadabout . . . Falstaff, Rockaby, Sweetheart, Tireless, Highlander, Pibroch, Chieftain, Crystal . . . Valkyrie, Beldame, Pickpocket, Tattler, Blackamoor, Dragoon . . . Tipster, Truthful, Hector, Melodious, Lucifer, Strident, Chorister, Lark, Cherokee, Hurricane . . . Phoebe, Fanciful, Juno, Linda.)

As they waited, old Bluebell and Rouster, of the plantation pack, could be heard speaking in the brake, and now and then an encouraging cheer: "Hie-on, rouse him!" The deep-throated music came nearer, the waiting pack grew tense. Suddenly their huntsman, cantering forward, turned in his saddle and shouted, "Hie-on! heu-eu, lads! Go get him!"

The fox flashed in a russet streak across a lane which skirted the brake. In the thicket the huntsman's velvet cap could be seen bobbing about. Seconds more, and Rouster, Bluebell, Burly, and Nimble crashed out of the heavy growth, followed by the fleetest of the guest pack. Then a swirl of hounds springing and tumbling in screaming haste to be clear of the underbrush. The combined packs swept across the lane and over a bramble hedge; the riders followed.

The baying had grown faint and died away and the last horseman disappeared over the low hills when two more riders emerged from the thicket. One was a white boy on a halfbred pony, the other a small Negro riding a mule with an old army saddle. They jogged on slowly, stopping at the top of the rise to listen for hounds. At a place where a scuppernong vine ran from its broken arbor and spread over a sagging rail fence, they waited. The last sweet grapes, golden and wrinkled, hung in clusters. The little Negro was reaching for a handful of grapes when his mule ceased cropping and stood with pricked ears.

"Hear anything?"

"Naw. But *he* do."

Presently the pony pricked his ears and tugged at the reins; then the cry of hounds became plainly audible. Half a mile away the hunt came into view, moving in a wide semicircle at a steady, swinging gallop. One red-coated rider, possibly deceived by the brambles which hid a wide, deep ditch, went down. The horse struggled up and went on, saddle empty. What became of the rider they could not tell. At the rail fence, which zigzagged its rambling course away from where the boys were, the hounds' speed was abruptly checked. The baying became doubtful, stopped altogether. A pair of wrens, which dwelt in a bush beside the fence, fluttered up and began an angry chattering. Their curses followed a shadow creeping along the top rail.

"Look!"

"Shut up! Keep still!"

The fox came on without fear, for he was moving downwind. He reached the cover of the scuppernong vine, then flattened himself down, head on paws, to rest. At last Old Burly owned that the fox had climbed upon the rails, but the huntsman called the hounds away in the wrong direction along the fence. The fox looked back with evident satisfaction at the pack's futile questing, and the huntsman was returning again when the boy's pony stamped with an impatient hoof and blew a loud breath. The fox looked up and saw. He rose slowly, deliberately, and gazed a long second before he dropped down from the top rail, looked back and walked casually away into the brambles.

Burly and Bluebell had gone back alone and were working out the trail together when the huntsman sounded his horn and called the pack along the fence, this time in the right direction. At the scuppernong vine, Rouster and Sheriff recovered the trail and, the rest harking to them, were away once more on a strong scent. They charged a tangle of catclaw vines which overgrew a dry ditch, and again they were running with all their forces, for they were close upon the fox. Rouster and Nimble had seen him—had chopped at his disappearing brush. The pack flew over the ground, catching the scent in the air. He ran in a burst of speed toward a pasture into which a drove of half-wild razorbacks had been harbored from the woodlands to fatten on peanuts before hog-killing time. Hounds saw him again in the open and ran almost mute in their frenzy to kill. The leading dogs were springing forward in great strides, nearly upon him, when his brush flashed under the strong wire fence of the hog-pasture. He ran through the filth of the swine lot, which destroyed his trail, and slipped out at the far side.

The huntsman galloped up on a blown horse, calling the pack, but ten or twelve hounds had already climbed the wire fence and were among the squealing, fighting razorbacks. When the pack had been assembled once more, one of the hounds, Tipster, was left behind. He crawled under a hedge, licking a wound which ran along flank and belly and from which protruded a purple fold of entrails, for he had been disemboweled by a boar.

The fox had put a quarter of a mile between his brush and the nose of the closest hound, now slowly puzzling out the trail. He trotted on for many yards in the dust of a cattle path that led to the pinelands, and skulked under a bush. His tongue lolled out. He was thirsty and rank and hot. There he did not stay, for instinct told him he was not yet safe, and if he lay still his legs would become stiff and useless for running. He trotted on again, dodging this way and that, pausing now and again to prick his ears and listen and test the breeze with his nose. At a runnel that flowed over a sandy bed and sparkled into a drain, he stopped, flacking once, twice, with a swollen tongue. He waded in and stood in the feeble current, letting it cleanse his heavily filthed brush; and having rid himself of the clots of swine dirt in his fell, he waded on several yards, lapping as he went. Even in his haste the fox paused long enough to reach for a frog with a deft paw. It wriggled free and escaped into a bed of moss.

Where the rillet became lost in meadow grasses, the fox emerged, sleek and small. He shook the water from him and became larger. After grooming himself briefly, he trotted on. Again he heard hounds speaking on his line, and his trot broke into a swinging lope. As he lolloped through a spinney a partridge hen with her big brood of late chicks, which had been sunning and fluffing themselves in a doodle-dust hole, flapped up and, turning, made as if to run at him, beating her wings angrily. The fox paused in his stride and seized the last of the chicks as they were disappearing with magical suddenness. He ran for four or five yards before dropping the bird.

He crossed two fields, squared by ditch and bramble-hedge, and, trotting again, followed a dim wagon trail leading toward a thicket of pines. Uncle Eli, a Negro woodchopper, had gone that way, creeping along on his cart drawn by a scrawny little ox. The ox-scent was rank, obliterating that left by the fox. But hounds had followed the line through the hedge of the first field. He heard Burly's voice, Drum's answering bass note, and then the rapid tongue of Rouster in the lead. Again he ran, overtaking the creeping ox-cart. He walked beneath it for a few yards. The sound of the pack, which now had crossed the second square and was clamoring along the road, caused the hair along his back to stand on end. He trembled in his misery, weaving back and forth, darting out from under the cart and in again.

The old Negro saw him at last and, shouting imprecations, whacked at him with a long stick.

"Git, you debbil! Hit de grit!"

The fox snarled, dashed away out of sight, turned, circled, and seeing the bitch Juno, ran back under the cart. This time he was not observed, for the driver was still muttering and waving in the direction he had first taken. Hounds were now panting along on each side of the cart, the wheels of which stirred up a dust. The dry, powdery nimbus made them sneeze, and the strong smell of ox caused them to forget the trail and keep their noses up.

A horseman's head showed beyond the hedge. His laboring horse cleared the ditch and pounded up. Another rider followed. Hounds were baying all around the cart; and the fox, seeking shelter, leapt to the feed rack beneath the floor boards, grasping with his paws and swinging himself inside. Meanwhile, the ox—made frantic by so much noise and confusion—humped his back and tried to buck and run, while the old Negro clung on, shouting and pointing with his goad.

The horsemen rode off in the direction he indicated, calling the dogs. All the pack responded except Rouster, who hung about under the cart. The other rider shouted: "G'on! Get away from there. G'on! 'Ware cart! Heu-heu-heu! hark!" and then swung his whip-lash. Rouster lifted his nose toward the hay-rack in which the fox crouched, peeping out. The hound gazed steadily until the pupils of his eyes became fixed upon a pointed muzzle and flattened ears and fangs. The hound sprang up, snapping at the challenging head, and struck his own head hard against the crossboards. This caused him to break into a storm of baying, at which the ox suddenly jerked the cart forward and ran away, bucking and bellowing: "Baw-aaaaaaaah! Bwuah-aaaaaaaah!"

Not realizing why Rouster had bayed beneath the cart, and because of the hound's evil reputation, the horseman swore at the hound and whipped him back toward where the rest of the pack quested for a trail now nonexistent. Rouster, with tail lowered and back bristling, growled resentment and kept looking away in the direction of the cart disappearing jerkily along the road.

The fox rode until the ox grew tired of running, and

then slipped out and away. He had looked into the teeth of his enemy and lived.

The huntsman called the pack and pushed on into a like-

ly thicket, hoping the lost line would be quickly found. "Heu-on! Wind him! Hustle 'm!"

The sounds of the horse and hound in the covert waked a large cub that had kenneled there since dawn. A young fox, never having been hunted before, he trotted back and forth, and in circles, crossing and recrossing his line in mingled fear and curiosity. When hounds came on the fresh scent, rising thickly, they stormed the covert in a fury. The horn sang *gone away*.

On a stretch of open grassland the pack rolled over the fleeing cub with a throaty rumble. He was chopped in Rouster's jaws, tossed into the air, caught, chewed, pulled, scragged, and broken. A warm smell of blood and guts rose and was blown away on the breeze. A horseman approached the boys and dabbed at their cheeks with a bit of bloody fur. "Now," he said, "let's hear you whoop!" The white boy grinned and let out a lusty yell, but the little Negro looked scared and, leaning down, vomited on the grass. When the man turned away the white boy said scornfully, "You fool, that wasn't *our* fox!"

The lights of the late-afternoon sun slanted across the fields, and the fields gave back the light in a glow of goldenrod and burnished sedge. Brightness shone briefly on the returning hunt, as hounds and horsemen moved across an open space in a hedge: on the pied pack; on the glistening, wet coat of a blaze-faced bay; on a silver whip-handle; on the mirroring, smooth-worn surface of saddle leather. Shafts of light ran obliquely on through the pines and were lost in a deepening gloom made audible with the fluttery, bird-piping rumor of night.

Uncurling in the tussock where he had rested, a fox still stiff from running stood up, stretched gratefully, and trotted out into the fields, flairing his nose for scent of cottontail or partridge. A note of the distant horn came faintly, calling a lost hound. The fox cocked an ear, sat back on his haunches and barked; and one last retreating sun-lance was caught and warmed an instant in the color of his coat, before the urgent day sped into darkness.

Aubade
(Forest of Compiegne: October)

R. P. Harriss

Now the swallows quit the eaves,
the wine-wind stirs the poplar leaves,
the forest mast is sweet to smell
and berries, as they blacken, swell;
old upland ways all glow like fire
beyond the paddock, stack and byre,
where pheasant hen and pheasant cock
make thrif-
ty rust-
lings in
the shock,
and beeches flaunt their pied costume
of minstrel's cloak and casquette-plume.
Across an elder brooding wold
the late year trails her cloth of gold,
touching each vineyard, croft, and tree,
each memorial verity,
the while her song wells soft and full
of ancientry inscrutable.
And deep in thicket, buck and boar
tread coverts secret, dim and hoar
where boar and buck and bird abode
ere Roland to the hunting rode.

Autumnal
(Carolina Low Country)

R. P. Harriss

The falling mast clacks on the floor of the forest,
The last sweet, shriveling scuppernong hangs ready to drop
At the deft shaking by the masked raccoon
And the plump partridge struts with distended crop.

In some far glade the black-nosed buck keeps thicket,
May-litter foxes are digging for mice in a furrow;
The chirring cricket is charming the lizard to sleep in his
    crevice,
The mole in his burrow.

Softly, softly
October is loitering over the spicy pinelands;
Softly,
Over the tops of the trees that listen for frost;
While subtler than parish bells with felt-covered clappers
A huntress in scarlet is calling the dappled hounds she has
    lost.

September Transient

R. P. Harriss

There is a mellow pleasantness about
The Negro village near the Southern town
On Autumn days. The talk flows in and out,
From house to house . . . "Sis Viney's man is down
Wi' chills en fever" . . . Dulcey's boys "has cotch
Th'ee han'some 'possums" . . . Wesley's "up in cote" . . .
He got six months for it. (He stole a watch) . . .
Rennie is "cookin' out" . . . Dan's bought a shoat . . .
The talk goes on. The children play and sing
As white youths do, only more quietly;
A sleeping hound, notched-eared and nondescript,
Sprawls on the sidewalk; every living thing,
Loving the sun, comes out-of-doors to see
Where laughing Autumn's feet have lightly tript.

To One in Trouble

R. P. Harriss

Now that this sadness has come home to you
And now that Sorrow has proved you of her brood,
I would have broken your highest solitude—
A handclasp, and a mumbled word or two.

But yesterday I saw you in your pride;
And miserable and weak, I turned aside
Lest we should meet,
And stumbled awkwardly down a different street.

November Rain

R. P. Harriss

The rain goes rattling down the hill,
A burly gust has stripped the fennel.
To its form the rabbit bounds;
The fox, to kennel.

On sodden field and soaking hedge
The cold rain pelts, the harsh winds follow,
While seek, with beating hearts, their nests—
Creatures of holt and whin and hollow.

Nose on paws, couchant, from sleep
Awaking in safe beds, they listen.
Outside: the storm sweeps down the hill,
The ice-drops glisten.

The old oak flails its twisted arms,
The hedge bends low, the saplings cower.
Beneath her churchyard stone sleeps one
Who cannot hear the shower.

An April rain, say who shall hear,
To wake and remember?
She soundly sleeps whose narrow bed was laid
Deep in November.

End of the Line

Robert A. Scott, Jr.

THE BUS stopped jerkily. An old lady started to get off, and I helped her down from the high step. She smiled. "Thank you," she said in a cracked voice. "What a nice day," her eyes said. "How nice of this marine to help me, and how good I feel, only a little tired. Spring is in the air." I smiled and said, "You're welcome." She was welcome—a beautiful day and no worries! "You're welcome," I said again.

Phil said something about chivalry as we got on. I laughed at myself. "Hell, it's spring." He gave the transfers to the driver, and the bus jerked ahead. All the seats were full. We stood holding the overhead rail, our arms raised in the familiar, awkward, self-conscious position. The people looked at us idly; a woman raised her eyes for a moment and went back to her magazine; a man smoking a cigar glanced at us, then continued to gaze at the enamel

"NO SMOKING" over the driver's head; a little girl stared with the unabashed, unveiled curiosity of the very young. There was a stolidity, almost a drowsiness about the people. They seemed lulled by the strong afternoon sun slanting in through the windows. There was very little talking, only the stop-start ring of coins, swish of doors, rise and fall of motor sounds.

Why were they so complacent, so dull? Couldn't they feel the age-old animal awakening of spring? I wanted to sing, curse, shout some obscenity to shock them alive. I whistled "Sweet Georgia Brown"—a few heads turned.

"Let's go to the end of the line," Phil said. "I don't like this thumbing in town."

"Okay," I said. "We ought to be there by seven if we have good luck."

"Yeah. Too hot for blouses today."

Two women got off at the next stop, and we took the front seat, facing across the bus. On the opposite seat was a thin, middle-aged woman flanked on one side by the staring girl and on the other by a little boy. I noticed him for the first time now.

He might have been seven, eight, or nine. He had blond hair, gleaming now in the sun, cut short except in the front, where it hung down in a slanting line across his forehead. Bright, alive blue eyes, small tilted nose, ears a little too big. He was dressed for his Saturday trip to town and was still excited by it. What struck me was his aliveness, his awareness, his impatience with the slowness of the bus. All my emotions seemed mirrored in his eyes, his parted lips, his whole excited face. To me he seemed the only person on the bus who cared that it was spring, and I was happy. I grinned, and he smiled back, his shy little boy's smile lighting up his whole face. There was a kinship between us. It seemed strengthened and intensified by the insensibility of the others.

We passed block after block, long streets lined with trees now budding palely in delicate greenness. Houses sitting in neatly squared lawns, people working among freshly blooming flowers. As we came into the outskirts of town, I noticed that the boy seemed to become more excited. He squirmed in his seat, folded and unfolded his arms across his small chest. He glanced nervously above his head. The woman, too, gathered her packages.

I guessed they were nearing their stop. The woman turned to the boy and nodded slightly. This was the signal they had been waiting for. He quickly scrambled up on the seat on his knees and reached for the buzzer cord. But before he could touch it, someone in the back pulled it, and the signal buzzed twice sharply in the bus.

He knelt for a second on the seat, then turned and climbed down. He seemed bewildered, a half-embarrassed smile on his face. "He—pulled it!" he said, meaning by that "he," no specific person, but whatever gigantic, unknown, inscrutable force had caused his disappointment. He seemed to hesitate as though, not realizing his frustration, he still intended to pull the signal. "Come on, Jimmy!" his mother said impatiently, and he followed her. I tried to catch his eye in sympathy, but he would not look at me. I felt somehow ashamed that I had seen his defeat. The bus started again.

"Look, Phil, do—well, do you really want to go?"

"Go? Why, hell, yes. Don't you? After all your talk."

"Oh—I—why, sure, sure I want to go—only—well, nothing."

"Well, my God, you sure are actin' funny: first you do; then you don't."

"Sure, Phil, I'm sorry, but let's get a coupla' beers at the filling station before we start."

"End of the line," the driver said.

For Thomas Wolfe

Virginia Hodges Tabler

O lost, and by the wind grieved, ghost, come back again.

The exultation and fury alike are over,
The insatiable earth-hunger is past, and all
The lonely search. Have you found the land you dreamed,
A place apart for those who are too tall?

Since you have brought to death so much of life—
Being by such fever and wonder driven,
And senses sharpened to delirium—
It may be that death in return has given
The clue you sought . . . the door unfound on earth,
A stone, a leaf, and the lost lane-end to heaven.

Run with the Pack

Virginia Hodges Tabler

If you would hold
One treasure back
From the claws of hate,
Run with the pack.

Confirm the false,
Speak the untrue,
Lest in a moment
They turn on you.

For if you once
Let them catch sight
Of the tender fawn
Of your delight,

Soon they will pick
Its bones too bare
To interest even
The scavenger.

The mild and gentle,
The young and small
Must live in terror
Or not at all.

Run with the pack,
Or run alone.
Be in at the death—
Or meet your own.

Radio

Newman I. White

Go and catch a falling star

Still stand uncaptured these, and rightly these:
Spring's timid tread among first-blooming trees;

The smell of salt where greening marshes stand;
The cold, clean starlight dropped on quiet land;

The rich, brown gleam of damp earth freshly turned;
The acridness of crisp leaves newly burned;

The million-mirrored flashes of bright sun
On wind-touched lakes that birch trees look upon;

The wet caress of gently driven snow;
The ruby red of ashen logs aglow;

The somnolent, sad wind's impassive rune
Heard from a bed of pine straw deeply strewn:

These still remain inviolate as when
They stirred strange cravings in fierce tribal men;

As though kind nature, planning ample dowers,
For other breeds of men, unkin to ours,

Had smiled upon us in our valiant play
And passed, unaltered, her undeviant way.

Barabbas to His Lieutenant on Mount Calvary

Newman I. White

"Of course," Barabbas said, "they let me go
And kept the Milksop to be crucified.
That's him there, in the middle. He denied
The ancient ritual—said a man might know
God's kingdom in himself, and that a blow
Should never be returned, and that the pride
Of priests was impious. Someone said he tried
To close the Temple. Well, if that be so

He earned his perch. Take me; am I a saint?
By Abraham, I'd rob a caravan
Tomorrow; I'm not squeamish, but I'm shocked
That any Jew should blaspheme, and attaint
The Temple, priests and Sabbath—such a man
Comes rightly to the cross—God is not mocked!"

Clais Returns

Newman I. White

Clais comes home to her dwelling;
What shall she have for delight?
Cornflowers, blue beyond telling,
Roses, sweet for the smelling,
Crocuses, rich for the sight.

Flowers were never for selling
Crimson or purple or white
Worthy of Clais tonight.
Clais comes home to her dwelling;
What shall she have for delight?

She shall have music, impelling
Softly to ease, and excelling
Sweetness of mortal or sprite. . . .
Harmony dies in the swelling,
Flowers die in the sight:
Clais comes home to her dwelling;
What shall she have for delight?

Mid-March, in Hope Valley

Newman I. White

Clais, today we see the breath-of-spring
Wreathing its stems with waxen gold and white,
And bridal-wreath's pale diffidence, half in fright,
Timidly take the lawn. We feel the sting
Of scarlet beauty in that smoldering thing,
Fire-in-the-bush. Soon, drowsily the night
Brings smell of blooming trees, and murmurous, slight
Half-noticed sounds—but when sharp voices fling

Far, far abroad what Aristophanes
Recorded long ago—that tremulous, shrill,
High-palpitant frog-boast from a hidden spot:
Step gently, Clais, lest we frighten these
Precarious singers whom a frost may kill,
And yet whose singing Time shall silence not.

A Man in Chicago

James C. Wickstrom

JOCKO was very short and stocky; his face was unshaven, sanguine, and weather-beaten. He wore a black leather cap, ear muffs, a worn-out pair of overshoes, wool gloves that had unraveled at several finger tips, and a heavy brown overcoat, threadbare and dirty, but roomy and comfortable. He was well bundled up, for it was cold that evening, as only Chicago can get cold, with the wind whipping off the Lake and swirling in among the skyscrapers, creating little gusts and whirlpools of biting wind, making eyes water, cheeks sting, and noses run. A woman in a black dress and short fur coat passed him trying to carry a purse and two packages and at the same time hold her hat on and her skirt down. Jocko mused to himself about the comical nature of women's clothing. Then he thought about his own clothing—his overcoat, a relic of the pocket-flask era, which had been given him by his friend Nick, who drove a Salvation Army truck—and he remembered the slip of paper in the pocket demanding in the curt phrasing of the city that he call by the news agency at seven thirty and see a Mr. Johnson. He was a little afraid of this ominous Mr. Johnson, and he wondered why he had to go see him. The night shift, he knew, took care of most of the complaints about circulation dropping off at certain corners, and he hoped that that was all it was. Every winter he had to go down there and tell them that it was getting too cold for people to stop at the Franklin Street stand when most of them were headed just across the river to the Union Station, where they could unbutton their coats and pull out their change without getting too cold. It was then six forty-five. In half an hour the rush would be over, such as it was, as he was explaining to himself in preparation for Mr. Johnson, with the cold weather and everyone hurrying to get to a warmer newsstand.

Around his belly was tied a little apron that had the name of one of the tabloids on it in big white letters. He was digging his gloved hands into it and letting the coins filter through them. There were a few half dollars, several quarters, many dimes and pennies as he fumbled through the pockets of the apron, but he discovered that he needed some nickels. He walked into a cigar store to get change, leaving his newsstand untended. Warm air felt good, but he didn't want to get too warm because he would start to sweat and then have to go right back into the cold again. A Jew was behind the counter smoking a cigar and talking with another pallid-faced Jew who was reading a paper—four-star final, Jocko noticed—as he listened.

". . . and dis Amy dame tells him dat for all she cares he can go climb a telephone pole, and so he sez,

'Listen, you bitch, after what I done fer yuz maybe yuz think yuz can get out of this thing without shellin' out a little,' and so she sez, 'Hell, yes, I think I can; jist what d'yuz think you can do about it,' so he sez, 'Here's what I can do about it,' and the son-of-a-bitch pulls out a gun."

That struck the Jew as funny, the idea of his friend pulling a gun on Amy, and so the rest of the speech was mingled with bursts of laughter and many short, concise, and meaningful motions with his hands. His friend also showed a slight attitude of disbelief by looking up from his paper, incredulous enough to inspire a full account of what happened.

"Oh, yeh," the Jew said, immediately reassuring him, "that crazy nut would do anything. He used to have money, y'know. But that's why he lost it: he's so Goddamn crazy. Oh, yeh, back in prohibition he used t'be filthy wit dough, y'know, back in the days when everyone with a bathtub was a chemist t'boot? Oh, yeh, he used t'be filthy wit it, but y'know, he went to duh dogs wit all his drinking. He drank too much of his own booze like I was tellin' yuz a while ago."

With this he leaned back and scowled at Jocko, who had been standing there making himself as noticeable as possible.

"What in hell d'yuh want?" the Jew asked him, though the question was not spoken as maliciously as it was worded. It was rather light, casual.

Jocko stepped forward quickly, timidly, and placed two half dollars on the counter, asking for a buck's worth of nickels. Reaching for the cash register, the Jew resumed his narrative.

"So, anyway, there he was wit Amy lookin' down the

barrel of a thirty-two and she's so scared she don't know what's comin' off: so she sez, 'Look here,' she sez, 'look here, now, I want to get this thing straightened out, see?' "

"Here's your nickels, Bud," turning to Jocko and handing him twenty nickels rolled up in a piece of yellow paper.

"So yuz can see how scared she was wit duh thirty-two pointed into her gut; so she sez. . . ."

Cold air again, and the door closing behind him, the voice a muffled hollow echo. Someone had taken a paper from the pile while he was gone and had left three cents. It made Jocko feel good to know that most of the people were honest, and it was only the dishonest ones who get into the papers with all their wild carryings-on.

He hated the Jews with all their "What in hell d'yuh want" and calling him "Bud" all the time. Dagoes were all right, because he was a Dago; and Micks were all right because he lived with some Micks, and they were all good Catholics, and there was one woman who sort of took care of him and fixed him a lunch bag every morning and washed up his shirts and underwear for him and let him use her family's bathtub once in a while. She charged him, of course, but it wasn't much. But for the life of him, Jocko couldn't see why in a country like America where everything is fairly nice and democratic there should be so many Jews to come around and ruin things. Jews and niggers. He couldn't see why there should be so many of them. He saw them by the hundreds every day, and he was certain he never saw the same one twice, because they all looked alike and he couldn't tell them apart anyway. And then the Jews came around with this guff about calling him "Bud" and asking him "What in hell d'yuh want." It grated on his nerves.

Walking over to the news agency, Jocko blended perfectly with everything in the city. He noticed little of it. All the noise and flashing lights and rumblings and distant clangings had been grinding into him for so many years that everything was perfectly natural and uninteresting. He did notice the smells, though. Every building or store had a different smell coming from it, even though the day was cold and windy and all the doors were closed. He liked the smell of nut shops most, then restaurants, dry goods stores, old vacant buildings that were drafty and dank, department stores, and the one he liked least of all was the smell that came from hotel lobbies. He began to wonder again about this Mr. Johnson and became a little frightened because he had never heard of him before.

The news agency was a barren room with a cement floor and some desks lined up in back. A pay window was on the right. He didn't like the idea of going to the news agency. There was always a bunch of kids around who sold newspapers too, and being reminded that he was part of their company was distasteful to him. There were other men his age, too, but most of them were blowhards who thought they were big shots when they got out on the street hollering headlines and attracting attention. A few of them he liked, because they had become docile and a little timid, as he had, but they never associated much except to exchange knowing glances in the news agency.

There was one old man—he must have been at least sixty—whom Jocko dreaded seeing and seemed invariably to run into. He saw him immediately as he walked in the door, sitting almost malignantly on a bench along the wall. Everyone around the news agency called him "Blinky." Blinky was a horrible sight because he was blind, and the sight of his face with those two little wrinkled-up knots of flesh where his eyes had been made Jocko wince every time he saw them. The blind man would get his papers every day, walk the streets with his tin cup, and when he had sold out he would walk until someone pointed him toward Madison Street, where he caught the street car. His only utterance was a feeble, quavering "Where am I?" which he asked whenever he bumped into someone. It made people fear, more than pity, him. The question grew in proportions, echoing in the hollow streets between gigantic buildings, like the frightened and bewildered scratchings of a rat in a maze. Just two little twisted knots of flesh and a shaking "Where am I?" The man haunted Jocko, just as his spirit haunted the city.

He reasoned that Mr. Johnson was one of the men sitting at a desk in the back of the room. He walked in that direction. A voice stopped him.

"Hey, what in hell d'yuh want?"

"Mr. Johnson" was all Jocko could manage to get out as he turned in the direction of the voice without noticing the face.

"Two desks back of me."

Mr. Johnson took the slip of paper that Jocko had received and glanced over it carefully, then, searching through a pile of papers on his desk, finally found what he was looking for.

"Yes, yes, here it is. Ah . . . Jocko, is that what they call you?" (Mr. Johnson was obviously a young college graduate, slightly weasel-faced and moronic looking, and was trying to be very democratic with Jocko. He made some hail-fellow-well-met and some we're-all-brothers-under-the-skin gestures with his facial expression and the intonation of his speech. But still, in spite of democracy, Mr. Johnson was anxious to impress upon Jocko that he was in control and was a little peeved at something.) "Well, Jocko, it seems that circulation has been dropping off up there at Franklin Street. Now, I want to be fair about this thing," he added energetically, "and if you have any explanation, I'll give it full consideration."

Jocko told him quickly with all the courage and energy he could muster that it was getting so cold that no one would stop at Franklin Street when he was headed for the Union Station. He appeared to be very much impressed with Mr. Johnson's geniality, but secretly he hated him. He knew that he had just got the job to learn something about newspapers from the bottom up and was probably the son of one of the big shots. He hated him, but he was too frightened to admit it to himself. Actually, Mr. Johnson was making an ass out of himself, trying to mingle with the masses and talk man to man about labor problems and be democratic and intelligent, talking with forty-year-old newsboys, most of whom were quite happy with their backs up against the wall. But Mr. Johnson found Jocko's story fairly plausible and let him go after some remarks about an improvement as soon as spring comes along, spring, spring, beautiful spring, chortle, chortle. Jocko did not appreciate Mr. Johnson's sense of humor.

On the Clark Street car, headed for the near North Side, Jocko remembered the Jew in the cigar store and the voice in the news agency and all the "What-in-hell-d'yuh-want" guff that he had taken that night. There was an advertisement in the front of the car that fascinated Jocko, and as he sat there, head swaying, he stared at it. It was a picture of a very happy, robust man with a highball in one hand

and a bottle of whiskey in the other, and underneath were the words "Old Underroof, A Gentleman's Drink." The clear, clean-cut lines of the picture held Jocko's eyes, and he liked the jocund expressiveness of the man drinking the highball. But the man's eyes soon became glaring, then vacant, and then they began to wither away, and the face wrinkled, and then there was nothing in the man's eyes but twisted flesh.

He decided that things were wearing on him a little too much and that all he needed was a little friendship. Nick would be glad to see him, he knew; he decided to drop in on Nick for a while before turning in. He and Nick talked a lot when they were together. Nick would be nice and friendly and maybe open up a bottle of his grape wine that he made himself. He had a good job—driving that Salvation Army truck—but he didn't swear by the Salvation Army. It was just a good job. Sometimes when he got a little high on his own home-made grape wine he would entertain Jocko by singing in a bawdy-drunk voice the song that began: "Put a nickel on the drum and be saved!"

The street car strained under a surge of electric power. They were crossing a bridge over the Chicago River. To the right he could see the Tribune Tower and the other brilliantly lighted buildings along Michigan Boulevard. There were lights in all the buildings, and the rooms were warm, and there were people in them reading the four-star final. It was almost eight o'clock: time for the *Tribune* to be coming out. The Lindbergh beacon swung across the sky in a giant circle. It was all too vast and fantastic for him to understand. He had grown indifferent to it. All he knew was that there was too much guff being thrown around by all the punks. All their Yiddish yappin' about "What in hell d'yuh want."

But Nick was good, warm, friendly. Once in a while they would go down to a burlesque theater on South State Street together and have a good time. South State Street was filthy and there was grit and dirt on the floor of the theaters that scraped under your feet and a few cockroaches running around, but they liked to watch the flabby girls take off their dresses and shake and dance around on the stage. Jocko had had a girl once, and he thought about her a lot, though he hated to admit it. Her name was Ruthie. She was an olive-skinned Dago girl of a certain lightly sensuous beauty, which gave one only a hint of voluptuousness and made her all the more enticing. He had gone with her until he found out that she had slipped him a dose, and he hadn't seen her since. That was hell, having the clap. He often remembered with horror the weeks he went through when it was torture to bend over to tie his shoe laces. All thoughts of women had made him a little ashamed since then; he felt ashamed even when he and Nick went down to see the strippers.

Nick lived in a room above a tavern owned by a man named Hank. Hank's place was about a block from where Jocko got off the street car. In order to get to Nick's room, Jocko would have to go through the tavern, into the kitchen, and up a flight of back stairs. He always felt embarrassed walking through the tavern with everyone glancing at him suspiciously and then into the kitchen where Hank's wife was usually cooking greasy hamburgers, but he knew it was all right. Just before he opened the door he stopped to light his pipe. If anyone said anything to him, he could take a few drags on his pipe and take it out of his mouth to stall for time, so he could think of something to say. He wasn't afraid; he just thought it was smart for a guy to think of the right thing to say before he opened his mouth, because there might be some drunks around who might start a fight at the drop of a hat. But he wasn't afraid. He began to say Hail-Marys to himself so that he wouldn't think about being afraid or about anything except getting up to Nick's room.

Hail Mary full of grace the Lord is with thee blessed art thou among women (the same stale smell of cigar smoke and flat beer that gets in the air from glasses standing around and the smell always goes with the green felt of pool tables and twenty-six games and the lights with green shades that make the smoke in the air look thick and hazy and the dice are turning dark and yellow-brown in spots just like Hank's teeth) and blessed is the fruit of thy womb Jesus (Jesus way down in your throat as he has heard the Father say it when he digs his double chin down into his white-starched collar and says Jesus with a lot of guts and depth and power and resonance to it and says Jesus in a weighty sonorous bass Jesus and hold on to it a little and sing it almost at the end and make it sound deep Jesus) Holy Mary Mother of God pray for us sinners now and at the hour. . . .

"What do you know, Jocko?"

Jocko stopped and took a few drags on his pipe and took it out of his mouth and looked in the direction of the voice. He found himself halfway along the bar, and he looked across it and there was Hank smiling at him.

"Oh, I don' know, Hank. Not much, I guess. Is Nick home?"

"I don't know, Jocko. Go up and see."

. . . Mother of God pray for us sinners now and at the hour of our death Amen. . . . Hail Mary full of grace blessed art thou among women blessed is the fruit (Hank's wife can make good hamburgers and she puts a lot of grease in the pan and smokes up the room a little and the whole place stinks of that fuzzy dead greasy odor almost like sweat) fruit of thy womb Jesus Holy Mary Mother of God pray for us sinners. . . . Nick's home 'cause there's light coming from under the crack of his door and there's the ripe old burning leaves oak smoking wood smell of his pipe and thank God for people like Nick who will talk to you without any of this cheap guff . . . that knock should bring him. . . . He's home. Yes, Christ he's home and he's been over there by the window smoking and reading the four-star final with his slippers on and his feet up on the window sill, because I can hear his rocker rocking as he leaves it and his footsteps are soft on the floor and soon he should. . . .

"Hello, Nick!"

Nick was there just as Jocko had pictured him before he opened the door. He smiled at Jocko and spoke to him casually.

"Hello, Jocko," he said. "What in hell d'yuh want?"

Two Alabama Wildcats

Julian Lee Rayford

I came upon two Alabama wildcats,
panting, panting in a cage.
And they bent upon me all the venom
in their flaming, yellow eyes,
their spirit no more diminished
than fire is tamed within a grate.
Two Alabama wildcats, glowering, smoldering,
in a rage that Death alone subdues.
And I thought, watching those inferno-eyes:
"Little brother, little sister, teach me,
endow me with this flame that devours
all cowardice, all resignation.
So many fears imprison me,
I need your flame of hatred
to burn my cages down."

A Certain Seclusion

Julian Lee Rayford

A certain seclusion there is,
A certain seclusion,
In the noise and confusion,
    noise and confusion
    of Chicago.
For, passing along Wabash Avenue,
    under the elevated trains,
And walking along with the streetcars,
    that roar explosively by . . .
You may chant a poem
    at the top of your voice.
And no one will know you have spoken.

Under the Mill

Julian Lee Rayford

The miller bags warm meal,
while in the cellar below him,
mocassins make obeisance
to the cogwheels.
The great cogs turned
by the trundling water wheel,
grind with a click
that charms the snakes,
and vibrates a century's cobwebs.
A bullfrog sits
on the blue earth floor,
blinking with the rhythm
and puffing with the click,
enchanted by the moccasins' metronomic sway.

You, Swiftly Fading

Vergil White

Du schnell vergehendes Daguerreotyp
In meinen langsamer vergehenden Händen.
—Rilke

OF NEW JERSEY he remembered well the house in Center Street, where his mother had spent her childhood and girlhood and where the Schmidt family used to sit eating "kaduffleglace" and sauerfleish under the gaslight in the kitchen. And how they drank beer there, his youngest uncle going to the parlor to play the piano and singing *Ach, du lieber Augustin!* The parlor was cold because the house was heated by stoves, and unless there was a fire in the dining room there was no heat in the parlor, but they never made a fire in the dining room unless Ellie and George and Josie and Leo and Emma and Ira were all there. The house in Center Street made him think of his poor grossvater, who had been a brewmaster and unfortunate enough to die long before prohibition was repealed. He remembered his grossvater as a silent little man with curly grey hair, who sat in the kitchen reading his newspaper. When he was young and the old man was alive, he never thought much about grosspop, as Josie's husband called him, but after the grossvater died, long after, he suddenly realized how lonely, how terribly lonely the man had been, because he found the same loneliness growing on him. "Poor grosspop," Leo would say, and down his beer in the kitchen at Center Street. And if you wanted to smoke, Ann would ask you to kindly get the hell outdoors unless it was winter, when you could go in the parlor and freeze. You couldn't even smoke in the toilet because tobacco made the place stink. In the summer the men would sit on the back porch smoking with Charley, who lived at home, and they would all say, "Jesus Christ, Charley, you must lead a hell of a life because you can't smoke in the house." And Charley would say, "Yeah, but what can I do? There ain't no use kickin' is there? Just gotta put up with it."

The house in Center Street had a brick-paved courtyard between the house and the barn, which wasn't used any more. The bricks came from a smokehouse which he dimly remembered: one day grosspop and Charley tore down the smokehouse and paved the courtyard with brick. They made a round flower bed in the center and a square flower bed by the fence for Pop's roses, which were the source of his delight in life. When he looked at the roses by the fence, he thought of his grossvater, who tended them with care perhaps because sometime in his youth in Germany he had known great beauty and kept the roses as a small reminder. All the people left in Center Street were materialists, who fumbled at such things as roses, and who remembered their father, John Christian Schmidt, as a fussy old man. A socialist he was, a socialist and a union member. Because he had wanted to be a humanitarian to the world, his children had never remembered him as a human being.

Over the mossy brick walk to the front gate, at the side of the house, grew a huge old grape vine on a rotting wood trellis. Grossvater used to sit under it in the summertime, the hard green grapes hanging over the curly gray head, ripening fruit and an old man.

Of his father's childhood and youth, few of the places remained. Of his father's family, fewer people. His father's family was old books, an old clock, old furniture about him every day. The Jersey Dutch. Farmers and hunters, with an occasional storekeeper for social prestige, and an occasional drunkard, mad geniuses who suffered, damned for their suffering. Of them he thought often, the disgraced outcasts whom no one understood. And he thought too, of his father's father, who turned in honor from the only thing he knew in life, to end his days humbly and bitterly. His father's father, only a hardware merchant, had committed an act of renunciation once, when his life was nearly spent, had turned from the store on Main Street and gained a new tallness. His wife never comprehended the act, nor his sons: they knew only that the family income was ruined. But he, the grandson, understood, and between the man dead and him existed this one live bond. It did not matter that when he was but an infant his father's father died: they knew each other by an act against the world.

He thought on the days of his own childhood, but with little pleasure. Even in memory they were filled with a kind of sadness, a continual frustration that he could never understand nor explain. He had played with other children, had read books, had built villages of bricks in his back yard. Yet always he was older than the other children, not in years, but by a sense of time that added his father's years and his grandfather's to his childish own. He thought of his childhood as an abasement of dignity, a period of torture. His worlds of fantasy were never complete escape from it: they increased the dignity and ended in greater humiliation. He was alone among his fellows, an aloof little figure scorning them as they scorned him.

And then, the family moved to a shady suburban street, where lived an odd assortment of Polacks, Germans, and people who called themselves Americans. The Polacks kept chickens and pigs, the Germans had a garden, and some of the people who called themselves Americans had continual family rows. Here he was no longer aloof: he entered into the neighborhood life, was accepted by a gang; and his days became an exciting round of warfare, huts, and automobiles made from baby-carriage wheels from the dumps. He remembered with particular pleasure a fight with water pistols, in which both he and his adversaries were drenched.

And the hooded woman. Only he, of all the gang, had seen her. She lived by herself, in a house with drawn shades, and no one knew her. For the milkman, little notes. Notes for the baker, the grocer, the laundry man. Yet once she showed herself to him. She stood at the door of the house and shouted to him to stop the baker's truck. The thin figure, the strange singing quality of its voice, and the horrible black veil over her face rooted him in a paralyzed ecstasy of fear. He stood mute and trembling, then felt his heavy feet moving, heard his boyish voice shouting to the baker man that *she* wanted him. Years afterwards, when he lived in another part of town, he learned that the mysterious woman, no longer a mystery, had died, and they had buried her with a veil still over the face eaten away by syphilis.

He remembered living by the swamp, where spring was wild iris, green brackish water, and a broken apple tree still blossoming. He remembered the swamp and the wide field by the side of the house where the snakes slithered through the grass with imperceptible sound, with only the grass waving to show they were there, and the big snapping turtles, and the pheasants in the autumn. The world of the swamp was a reptilian paradise, where handsome water snakes, snapping turtles, newts, and lizards lived lazily in stinking water that dwindled and stank more viciously in summer when the cicadas droned all morning in the tall trees on the other side of the field. And the cicadas and the wind in the long grass sang on into memory, into a world where bright reptilian eyes no longer stared knowingly, where the wind was caught between houses and the exuberance of seasons in the fields was suspended.

So memory inched back to Center Street and the laughter there, and the bitterness and bitching. For in Center Street all the people cherished regrets and defeats and petty hatreds, which had become a way of easing the monotony of living in Center Street seven days a week and sitting under the gaslight in the kitchen at night, talking or sleeping or drinking beer. The house in Center Street was no personal thing: it was a symbol of the old Germans and their way of life, which gradually slipped from them while they were living and which their children could not recapture. Center Street was not a street: it was a neighborhood, a vast city in America where this loss was a continual process and the old meanings disappeared. And because there was nothing but movies and beer, after prohibition, to take their place, life had no meaning, and everybody sat in the kitchen under the gaslight and cursed and complained and envied everybody who did not live in Center Street.

Then family by family the Germans had moved away, and the Italians came to take their place. Because the Germans detested the Italians, mistrusted their ways, and hated the sound of their church bells, the Germans kept moving away, until only three, two, one family was left. And finally, a tired old German woman packed her clothes and furniture and went to live with her daughter, so there were no more Germans in the neighborhood, and the bells of the Italian Church rang louder than ever.

It was because so much changed and turned beyond returning that he remembered, and yesterday became important for what it had been since it could not again be.

And from the flowering of words and images in his mind he could build a structure that was neither past nor present, but was becoming a vaster edifice, of power, not impotence, and had the roots of its meaning in the future. In the beginning was only a word which was not God, but he. And from the beginning the word expanded in search of a cosmos beyond touching, tasting, and seeing; and beyond the cosmos of the structure that other people had made to limit the universe. And already he could experience a tree as well as hunger and was learning to feel beyond feeling, although the word was a little behind this.

Island Boy

John Schaffner

Come to these sands, come to these cupping waves
that churn their pretty scallops on the shore.
Here sea and land untiringly embrace—
taking and giving, taking and giving—And more
and more and more the seabirds cry. And more,
the wind above the dunes. From dawn and peace
to midnight's fury, these are lovers locked
together, and no fear of morning, ease
from the long ecstatic pain, shall move
them. Only ebb and flow, ebb and flow—
to the world's end, song of wave and shore.

Come to these sands, you and I shall learn
all that the wind can teach us—of the grass
in fervency bowed down before its stride;
of those white hands that gently stroke the sky,
the clouds; and why vine leaves, once dark, must burn
because the cold has pressed its lip—even
it may be given us to know some of
this timeless passion of the land and sea.

The Golden Gazelle

John Schaffner

Down a quiet Thibetan valley
hurtled too hard for a scream
a quivering sudden thing flew
like a dream
all bronze in a flash.
And there clashed as it fled
over lava and ash
two great thudding wings of a bird on its head;
there throbbed in its brain
two claws and a beak.
It poured to the sky,
glazed and limpid with pain,
a gazelle's golden eye.
It uttered no cry
no sound but the beat of the patter
of tiny horned feet
and the gentle sweet spatter
of blood
upon dust.
Swift as its flight
it stopped, shivered, and fell.
Then, a hot shriek,
a shot upward like light,
and the eagle hung high
(gorged with brain of gazelle)
in the bell of the sky.
And the golden gazelle was a spot
in the waste of the Thibetan plain.

The Hurricane

Richard Austin Smith

SOREN dropped his axe and sat down at the foot of a tall, thick cedar. Wearily, he mopped his brow. Here it was September and this the hottest day for three months. Air heavy and lifeless, the same as last night. Not even enough breeze for gulls to soar, and they floated on the flat water, quarreling. There was a sultry, wet feeling to the atmosphere unlike the usual sea damp. Little currents of air kept striking his face and hands, but the trees about him were still. All morning cirrus clouds had traveled at high speed across a sky blue with wind, and yet the ocean below was steady as a tide pool.

Many things seemed to be unleashed and in motion, yet no mark of them was to be seen. Yesterday strange, transparent sea-creatures had filled the inlet and even now lay thick upon the beaches, where a strong tide had carried them inland. These he had seen only once before and then far at sea. At noon, dark, greasy clouds began gathering; and gradually the colors of forest and fields, the gray of rock and the subdued green of spear grass took on the brilliant, almost electric shades that presage storm. A change for better or for worse, he reasoned from long experience on the Banks, should have come with the turn of the tide. But no breeze stirred, and the glass continued its steady fall.

Stretching out full length under the tree, Soren impatiently tugged at his ear. Must be changes of pressure, the way he had to swallow to keep it open. Like standing in the entrance of a tunnel when a train was on the way through. Then, suddenly, quietly, it began to rain. First a few scattered drops, bending the green ferns at his feet. Off in the distance, wind began to stir the trees. Almost before his axe was under his arm and he was running for the cliff-path, he heard its sound sharpen. Shrill, high-pitched, a music of steel surrounded by a hundred minor notes, it swept up from the southeast. The trees parted before it like the blown fur of a kitten.

Running full speed now in the driving rain, he made out the path before him. The heavy drops made a knee-high fountain as they bounced off the hard-packed clay. As he climbed, he could hear the wind coming up behind him. It stormed across the open meadow, hurled the countless ravines, left small whirlwinds spinning along their grassy bottoms, and launched itself with a mighty roar against the cliff-head. The impact of that meeting shook the massive columns of rain like cannon-fire. There was a moment of breathless calm; then with the force of a thunderbolt it broke full upon him. The rain, now almost horizontal, stabbed unmercifully at his back. Desperately he clung to the cliff wall, inching his way up the path. At every step the wind, acting with the ferocity of a water-spout, tried to spin him away from the lee of the cliff. But, digging his fingers into the crevices, he crept on. Half-way to the top, he met Suzanne, her dark hair black with rain, yet her eyes alight with that curious still fire that burned in them when danger was at hand. Silently, he patted her arm, and they went on together. Near the top of the cliff she stopped and pointed out to sea. Through the rain he saw what seemed to be a great fog bank sweeping across the water. On it came, fifty feet high, swallowing wave trough and wave crest in its path to the island. As it drew nearer they saw in a kind of paralyzing wonder that it was no fog at all, but a great plateau of water, raised high above the ocean surface and moving over it with the speed of an arrow. Unconsciously, they braced themselves as the giant wave struck the eastern rocks. The whole end of the island vanished in a green maelstrom. Suzanne shuddered involuntarily, wincing almost as if she herself had received the impact. Then gradually they saw the

water, far inland, begin to recede and the black rocks like seals push their way upward through the sea.

When at last they reached the house, the storm had taken on the singing, high-pitched note of a hurricane. The tiny plateau had been swept clean of everything movable—benches, woodpile, fish racks, wheelbarrow. Crawling on hands and knees, they made their way to the house's eastern wall where the great iron-bound shutters swung wildly in the wind. Using all his strength, Soren closed and fastened one. But Suzanne was unequal to the other, and it shook her as a terrier shakes a stick. At length they fastened it too, and crawled into the warm, dry kitchen.

For three days and nights the storm blew. There was little rest, for the wind outside raged with unceasing fury. Sleep and waking hours merged formlessly together. After a while even alertness to danger ran slowly, like a river under ice.

Most of the time was spent in the tiny observation tower on the second floor. Through its windows, however pitted by windblown sand, the struggle of sea, rock, and wind was clearly seen. After the first few hours, the normal outlines of the island had been replaced by mountainous green seas. The old lighthouse at land's end lay now five fathoms below the great combers that thundered inland to the very knoll below the house. Sometimes their churning mass climbed half-way up the slope and flung a scarf of spray that beat against the panes like drumfire. Huge boulders, many of them tons in burden, were flung up from the sea bottom. The next instant a mountain of foam, thinly masking the green sinews that stretched a quarter mile behind it, reached out and they were gone.

But if the sea shattered the land and the wave crests cut

white channels through the low-lying heavens, it seemed also at war with itself. Wave fought wave, the great ones —rising hill-like above the spindrift—immediately dashing against each other before their terrible assault on the land. Shock-born from these, smaller billows ran wildly through the maelstrom, momently girding a level field of foam, or met with others in death lock, rising into thin, high walls which the hurricane wind immediately blew into nothingness.

To the watchers in the shaken house, the wind alone seemed invincible. It worked its will alike on land and sea. Scarcely a tree stood on the eastern end of the island. Even those in the shelter of the house leaned crazily. Leaf ribs, blown bare of tissue, vibrated like antennae on the twisted branches. Besides the high, shrill whistle, steady as the rain beating upon the roof, there were intermittent gusts of great intensity. Soren and Suzanne could hear them start afar off, their deep, low roar gradually taking on volume. When they struck the house, the stout timbers creaked and groaned like a ship in a seaway. Water ran in thin trickles across the floor.

Through all this Suzanne maintained an impenetrable calm, talking little, doing much. Somehow she kept the stove going despite the terrific downdraft in the chimney and frequent stoppages from rockweed. And somehow too she got hot food and freshly dried blankets. Soren wondered even in this time of danger at the subtle tenderness she showed for him. Demonstration was so much a part of her that subtlety seemed strangely foreign and restrained, as unnatural as her deliberate calm. Often he awoke from the innumerable cat naps to find her staring at him wistfully. And he had taken her into his arms and held her to him until the soft fingertips on his neck told him she was herself again. But her calm was unchanging, even as his own excitement mounted with the growing fury of the sea. When terror-stricken sea birds thundered against the roof and came hurtling through the lighted windows, hers was the steadier hand; it was she who carried the stunned birds to the shed behind the kitchen while Soren stood there at the shattered panes listening wildly to the sea's roar.

On the afternoon of the fourth day the storm stopped as suddenly as it had begun. The sun came out and the sky cleared. Soren and Suzanne, with a strong music singing within them, set about cleaning their house. Food, Christensen's books, wet clothes and blankets—all were spread outside in the warm air. Then, almost fearfully, Suzanne took Soren by the hand and together they walked back of the house to the tiny knoll.

"You can see where it hit the big ones," Suzanne said, pointing out the thick western stands. "The tops are out of them all."

"Looks like a big man walked through the whole forest, swinging his shoulders."

Suzanne smiled a little: "Well, if they're not matchwood, it'll mean less felling for you."

"Oh, don't worry about me." Soren laughed, pulling her to him. "The cliff and the ridge saved enough fine trees to put a five-year callus on these hands."

"There're plenty down," she said, her voice low. "And every one's a part of us. The bitter sea."

"Oh, darling, don't take on so." He looked at her, concern clouding his face. "The cut timber's not been harmed. It was the seaward end that took the most punishment. Here"—turning her around—"look, the worst damage was done where it didn't matter. That clump of bull saplings is down, but I'd never of cut them anyway. And the beach's been moved a hundred yards. But mostly the sea just chewed up the turf and bit into the rock. And biting rock doesn't even do the sea any good. Does it?"

The dark eyes lightened.

"And—Great Dogfish! The boat! I bet there isn't a splinter left of her. I'd better look."

"No trouble making a raft," Suzanne called after him, regaining her usual gaiety.

But Soren did not hear her and continued on his plunging, loose-jointed descent. At the foot of the path he found little left of the old beach. Red earth and rock, scoured clean, were all that remained of it. Of the boat there was nothing beyond the frayed and sodden rope-end still tied to its rock-set mooring ring. Aimlessly he walked across the raw, red earth to where a willful sea had spread the stolen sand contours as smooth as those on the old beach. It was almost as if he expected to find the boat there, miraculously intact. But the sands were bare save for great patches of rockweed and the limp bodies of sea birds. And so he walked on, called unconsciously by the deep boom of the still-heavy surf as it flooded through the caves on the eastern shores. On the way he passed the grove of pines; not one was standing. Their roots, white and nerve-like, hung high above the tumbled soil. And Soren felt in his heart a terrible, silent fear that the sea had really come upon the land.

Glancing now and again at the trampled grasses or the great boulders, some so new from the bottom that shellfish still clung to their sides, Soren walked on. At last, coming to Eastern Point where the black rocks dropped abruptly into the surf, Soren stood quietly, listening. The sea-noises seemed to wall him in, transfixing him with the thunder of the great, green waves battering the rocks at his feet. Gradually, as if a floodgate were opening, he felt the sea sweep through his mind. The heavy, erratic rhythms of the surf he seemed to understand and felt them beating in his blood. Each wave took away a little more of himself, as a statue of salt slowly vanishes in a wild sea. Then afar off he heard Suzanne's clear voice calling and turned to see her running toward him across the rocks. With her name sweet upon his lips, Soren turned and held out his hand. Her eyes were alight as she touched his fingers. Suddenly the black rock cracked and crumbled beneath her feet. A new roaring shook the air. For an instant her eyes looked at him with a strange deep look, and then she dropped like a stone into the boiling cauldron below. For a moment Soren swayed on the edge, the roar of the sea dead in his ears. Life seemed to have come to a crashing stop. Wild fires raged through his mind. Swirling black smoke obscured his reason. The veins dropped away to nothingness, and his brain went down in a welter of blood. Then, he jumped. As he did so, more rock collapsed from the sides, great ragged chunks of it. The churning sea reached up for the man and the hurtling fragments, and they disappeared together in a pillar of green spume. Wildly Soren's hands reached out for Suzanne. Sand stabbed at his eyes. Savage currents coiled about his body, smashing it against the narrow sides. Somewhere here! Somewhere in this small space! Perhaps at the bottom, where the sea surged in! Down he swam through water stiff as glass. Each empty sweep of his hands tightened the fear about his heart. If only he could touch her, could catch some glimpse of her in the murk ahead! Suddenly a great, black shape shot by, coming to rest almost in front of him. The water grew still; the tentacles of the sea fell away from his body. Gropingly, his hands felt for the thing. Rock! Frenzy powered his muscles; fingers pulled and tore at the massive slab. It *must* move! The passage through to the sea *must* be opened! Lungs writhing, heart beating itself to pieces against his ribs, he tugged until the blood gushed from his nose. But the rock moved not. Its weight sealed the narrow passage like the door of a vault. At last Soren, consciousness fading within him, rose logily to the surface. The water was pond-still around him. The sharp air struck at his raw lungs. Half-conscious, he pulled himself up the side, blood striping the rock after him. Heartbreak broke the seal on the glazed eyes. The water was so quiet now. Nothing. . . . No trace. . . . Down there, nothing. . . .

For a long time Soren lay there exhausted, looking at the rocky chasm. How secretly the sea must have worked, hollowing out this chamber. Coming here in storm to vent its hidden rage, carving the arched dome to paper thinness.

Gradually his strength came back, and with it the sword of anguish sharpened. Each pulse-beat stabbed out her name . . . Suzanne . . . Suzanne . . . Suzanne . . . Suzanne . . . until his whole body shuddered to it. He seemed to feel himself spinning aimlessly through space without direction or bearings. He felt as if heart and mind had been torn from his body, and their nerves, like the white treeroots, left dangling in thin air. And nothing, nothing left. Water in the pool was clear now, to the very bottom. Suzanne had vanished almost as if she had never been. The roar of the surf, the clear sky, the stolid rock—all unchanged—

shook his reason with the thought that nothing could have happened. Then crystal clear he saw the dark, sea-flooded passages. The image of her there wrung from him a great cry. Like a madman, he stamped upon the rock, seeking another thin-walled cavern. But the ledges were solid and each wild leap ended on live stone. Almost crazy now he ran from one narrow inlet to another, searching, searching for her. Twilight came and left him alone there with the night on Eastern Point.

Through the darkness he stumbled on. Even dead he must find her. And spurred if by so black a hope he crept back and forth across the rocks until the boom of surf in the caves rose to thunder and the sea was white with phosphorescence. Then, exhaustion claimed him and he fell headlong upon the spray-wet stone.

Soren awakened in broad daylight, a rough hand shaking him by the shoulder.

"Hey there, come out of it! That's better now. Have a nip of this."

He grasped the bottle and took a long pull. The liquor warmed him, steadied his mind.

"Where're you from?" he asked, running the words together weakly.

"Lighthouse Service," answered the older of the two men. "Me'n Clark came to fix the beacon. Storm blowed it out, I guess."

"Ain't there more'n you here?" questioned his companion.

"There was," Soren said, the whole force of his being steadying the two words.

Clark scraped his boots across the rock, uncomfortably.

"We'll be going back to Searsport now," said the older one, gently. "There's plenty of room if you care to come."

An uncontrollable desire to fly the place gripped Soren's heart. Muttering: "Wait," he shambled off toward the house. It was the work of an instant to pack the clothes and the little money; then, closing the great door, he started down the path. He had gone only a few paces before the cries of the imprisoned sea birds stopped him. Hurriedly opening the tool shed, he released them, then ran almost in panic toward the beach.

The lighthouse men were waiting in their dory when he got there. Silently they put out for the small schooner anchored just beyond the reef. Soren, sickness in his heart, turned for a last look at the island. High over the quiet house, the freed birds were winging their way, once again, out to sea.

Omens and Tokens

Ralph Nash

In new moon, in dark of the fishfin moon
find out haunts of fishes, find
old Slabsides goggling at florins and the seachest
bound in brass, hung in the cross of currents
at the sign of the waving fin.

In dark of moon, the loamclot moon,
crumble the weightless clod and
wait no answer:
from pebble dropped at fork of brook and branch
under the bridge at crossroads, wait no answer's
consequence, except its chink
disturb the foxes come to drink
—in dark of moon, with dark and dripping muzzle.

Elegy

Ralph Nash

Drowned, drowned in these waters under reaching branches
—green stipple, white stipple, shimmer without color,
hair's full float among the delicate separate rootlets
granulets clinging, white sandsift, white among yellow.

Whenso death and whereso with his current
beareth the spirit, yet remaineth beauty
lapt in a lisp of water, a consecration
not for the years' forgetting—
drought in the rivermouth, dry
stones clacking,
old talk from old branches.

Sandpiper tracking the landspit lightly,
yet when the wind pipes hollow through your bones
I'll sing to my love beneath the frosted thorn
the songs of summer: today and yesterday,
feathers and dust and a ghostly piping—
death by water and a dark
swirl of laughter,
old songs from old corpses.

Esthetic Experience

Ethel Davis Ramsay

Beauty to her was less in the rough, gray thunder
Than in the little waves along the shoal;
Beauty to her was less of words than wonder,
Less wonder than a triumphing of soul.

In lonely intervals of white desire
Her body fell a prey to Beauty's plunder.
Afar, pale signals seemed her spirit's fire—
Her more articulate ashes told our blunder.

Early Winter

William Snitger

THE WIND coming down from the north shook a few leaves loose from the oak trees and bent the pines on the hills surrounding the village. Each gust of cold air was more forceful and more bitter than the last, and the trees stiffened and relaxed as the wind hit them. The sun was not visible through the gray clouds, but the light forced its way over the countryside and grimly announced another day to the villagers.

Kolya, walking along the main street of the village, felt a warm glow tingling inside of him in spite of the icy air that brushed against his face. Clutching the package in his arms a little tighter, he tried to imagine little Petasha's face when he would open the box. Ten years ago Petasha had been born, and since that day Kolya had been more than a godfather: he had treated the child as if he were his own. Kolya remembered that the day ten years ago had been much warmer. Winter comes earlier every year, he thought. He could see a few candles flickering inside of the small houses along the main street, and he wondered how long the Sumarakovs had been up. It was almost seven o'clock now; and because Petasha's older brother, Alexander, had to leave for the army at eleven, the celebration was going to take place around eight o'clock. Petasha's mother had insisted on having the occasion just as it had always been, regardless of the war. "We will have a birthday breakfast for Petasha and a farewell party for Alexander at the same time. I will not let the war take that away from me," she had said defiantly.

Kolya realized that this would probably be the last time they would all sit down at the same table, and this thought darkened his happiness. If it could only be like the other birthdays, he thought, when there was plenty to eat and everyone was gay and carefree, and there was no war to spoil everything, at least, no war like this one. There had been other wars, but they had not affected the people in the village as much as this one—this great war! This war of machines and rapid destruction! This war that was taking all the young men and . . . .

The cold wind seemed to be going right through his small body, and he quickened his pace. When he turned down a small dirt road at the end of the main street, he could see a thin line of smoke coming from the chimney of the Sumarakovs' house. It was the largest house in the village—"Too large," Anna Sumarakov insisted. "It takes too much wood to heat it, and there is too much work to do!" But nevertheless she was as proud of it as her husband and worked continually to keep it spotless. Kolya remembered the day they moved into the house. Stepan had had it built months before the wedding, and when he took Anna there as his bride, it was completely furnished. There was a housewarming the night of the marriage, and Kolya had helped Stepan decorate the living room with large pine branches, flowers, and colored paper. After the party Kolya was the last one to leave; and as he stood in the doorway watching the happy faces of his two friends, he said, "I hope you find happiness in your home. I know you will." That was nearly twenty years ago, and both Kolya and Stepan were now forty-seven.

As he walked up the stone walk to the front door, he suddenly noticed how much the house had changed. The shutters had been taken off years ago, and the small wing, which had been added when Petasha was born, seemed to throw the house off balance. Kolya sighed, "I've changed too. My hair isn't bushy and black any more, and I'm getting thin. No wonder Anna insists that I eat so much when I visit. Things change so gradually you barely notice, and then one day your realization startles you."

There mounted in his mind a myriad of memories of the days he had known in this house, days of happiness and days of tragedy. He had watched the family grow and had been a constant friend and helper for twenty years. He shared both their happiness and their sorrow. When the third child died in infancy, Kolya dug the grave and made all the arrangements for the funeral—he was to have been the boy's godfather. When Petasha was born, he and Stepan sat up all night drinking; and when morning came they both staggered through the village shouting as loud as they could, "It's a boy! It's a boy!" Anna told them indignantly that she would never be able to face the villagers again, but when she was alone nursing her little

Petasha, she would whisper, "You, child, have the most wonderful father and godfather in all of Russia."

Kolya knocked on the door and waited for Anna to let him in. When she opened the door, she smiled and said, "I knew you would come early. I've made a cup of hot tea. Come into the dining room."

She was wearing her usual gray dress that almost touched the floor, but over it she had a bright-flowered apron with a border of fine lace around the hem. Her eyes were calm, and her broad face was framed with two long braids of hair, which were pinned around her head. Her rough hands moved efficiently in preparing the tea for Kolya.

"Where are the rest?"

She placed the tea on the table and sat down across from him. "Petasha went with his father and Alexander to the post office to make the arrangements for Alexander's leaving." Her voice faltered momentarily, then she continued. "Natalie is preparing a rice pudding in the kitchen. She insists on doing it by herself. She wants to surprise Petasha. The others should be back soon."

Kolya sipped the hot tea for a while. "Perhaps you'd better hide this before they get back." And he gave the package to Anna. She had been staring at it ever since he entered the house; now she turned and looked into his eyes. Kolya pretended not to notice.

"Dear friend," she said, and took the package into the kitchen.

Natalie followed her mother back into the dining room, walked around to Kolya, and kissed him on the forehead. She was a large girl, very much like her mother, and her eyes were the kindest and bluest that Kolya had ever seen. He often told her, "You have your mother's eyes!" Her seventeenth birthday had been two weeks ago, and Kolya had not seen her since then.

"Natasha, you get prettier every day!"

She blushed and looked at her mother.

"Nonsense," Anna replied. "Who wants to be pretty? She must learn to be a better cook and housekeeper! I can't do all the work!"

"But Mother," Natalie cried, "I have just made the most beautiful rice pudding you've ever seen!"

Anna laughed boisterously. "But we don't eat rice pudding every day of the week! Now, set the table and make sure the ham doesn't burn."

Natalie moved reluctantly toward the kitchen, murmuring, "Wait until you see my pudding."

Anna and Kolya laughed, and Anna said, "She *is* pretty, Kolya, but what good will it do her with all the men leaving?"

"You are too practical, Anna."

"It's a good thing someone in this family is practical."

She began to take the empty teacups into the kitchen; and as Kolya looked around the room at the heavy dark wood furniture and the small fire in the grate at the end of the room, he heard Stepan and his two sons coming up the walk. When they entered, the house took on new warmth. Petasha ran into the dining room laughing, "Kolya? Is Kolya here yet?"

"Well," greeted Kolya, taking the child in his arms and hugging him, "how is my little birthday boy?"

Petasha smiled and fixed his black eyes on Kolya. "I told Daddy you'd be here."

Kolya glanced over Petasha's head at the two older men standing in the doorway watching the scene. Alexander was not as tall as his father, but they both had the intense dark eyes, the long arms, and the broad, slanting foreheads that seemed to mark a Sumarakov. Stepan's eyes met Kolya's, and there was understanding between them that came from their lifelong friendship. Kolya knew how much it meant to Stepan to say goodbye to his older son. They had worked with each other ever since Alexander was old enough to go in the fields. Stepan and Kolya together had watched Alexander's love for the land increase each day. Stepan had often said to Kolya, "That boy will be a great farmer some day. Not like you and me, really great. He loves the land. Russia is part of him!"

Stepan and Alexander shook hands with Kolya, then hung their coats over a chair by the fire. Stepan's husky voice called out, "If we don't get some food soon, I'm going to eat Petasha!"

Anna laughed and appeared in the doorway to the kitchen with a large platter of bread and butter. She glanced at Alexander and asked, "Are they still coming to get you boys at eleven?"

"Yes. They expect the trucks to come through the village around eleven."

Anna's voice was cheerful again. "Everyone sit down. Kolya, you sit next to Petasha. Natalie and I will have things ready in a few minutes."

The men sat around the table and began to discuss the sudden change in weather.

"I hear they're sending us to the South," Alexander said to Kolya. "The winters aren't as bad there."

Presently Anna and Natalie came in the room, carrying large plates of eggs and baked ham. Everyone ate with relish; Kolya was amazed at his own appetite, and he needed no coaxing from Anna, who seemed to be in both the kitchen and the dining room at the same time during the meal. No one said anything when Alexander refused a second helping of eggs and ham. The climax of the occasion came when Natalie brought in her rice pudding and Anna followed her with three packages, one of them being Kolya's. Petasha stared at them and then at his plate.

"First we will eat Natalie's great pudding," Anna laughed, "and then we will see if Petasha has been a good boy or not."

"See," Natalie continued, "what I've made for you, Petasha! Imagine! Rice pudding for breakfast. What would the people think!"

They poured the rich cream over the pudding and finished the meal. Everyone complimented Natalie, and even Anna admitted that it was almost as good as her own pudding.

"Anna, you know you are jealous because it is better than yours," Stepan said, winking at Petasha, who giggled and glanced again at the packages in the middle of the table.

"Now," Anna said ignoring her husband, "open your gifts and let us see what you got, Petasha. But the little box is for Alexander."

The older boy turned towards his mother as if he were trying to memorize how she looked. She smiled back at him, and in an instant she saw his whole life pass before her eyes. Kolya knew what she was thinking: first, of the small red-faced baby, then of the little boy going to school, then of the boy working with his father in the field, and now of the young man going off to war. She tried to push these thoughts from her mind and began to help Petasha unwrap his gifts. In the first box was a heavy winter sweater and a small toy gun that his father had carved out of wood. Anna had said to her husband when he showed her the gun, "Why do you want to give him that? He's only a child and shouldn't even think about such things yet." But Stepan had answered, "In Russia children grow up quickly."

Petasha knew he was getting the sweater—he had seen his mother working on it many evenings by the candle, but the toy gun was a complete surprise. How the other boys would envy him! Now he could really play "war."

"Guess who the other one is from?" asked Natalie as her mother placed the large package in front of Petasha.

"I know," he said. "Kolya." And he turned and smiled at the man at his side.

"Well, open it. Let's see what it is!"

"Such a large package!"

Petasha's tiny fingers worked with the string, and finally he opened the box. When he saw the new leather boots, both his mouth and his eyes opened wide.

"Oh," cried Anna, "Kolya, why did you spend so much money? You shouldn't have! They're beautiful, aren't they?"

"They are the finest boots I have even seen," added Stepan.

Everyone gathered around Petasha, felt the smooth leather, and complimented Kolya on his gift.

"Aren't you going to thank your godfather?"

Petasha turned his head towards Kolya, who could see that the boy was almost ready to cry.

"Oh, thank you, dear Kolya," he stammered.

"I hoped you would like them. I was afraid they

wouldn't arrive in time for the party. But what about Alexander's gift?"

The older boy reached out and took the small package. It contained a beautiful scarf of three different colors with his name embroidered on one side. His expression remained the same for a moment; then he turned and kissed his mother on the cheek.

"I shall cherish it always."

There was a silence for a few seconds; then Anna spoke.

"Well, you men sit around the fire and talk. Natalie and I will wash the dishes in a hurry. Petasha, you needn't help today. Stay and talk to Kolya."

Kolya put the boy on his lap and helped him try on the boots.

"Why, they fit perfectly, Kolya! How did you know my size?"

"I know many things about you, Petasha."

Stepan put several large logs on the fire and sat down to watch the glowing flames. Alexander stood by the window which faced the village and silently drew on his pipe. The crackling of the fire and the tinkling of the dishes were the only sounds in the house. But the loneliness of each person seemed to pound against his ears. There was something leaving all of them, something more than Alexander; something was going out of their lives which would never come back. The Sumarakovs were losing one of their family, and a way of living was going with him. Even Petasha felt that the party had been much different from the others he could remember. The clock on the mantle over the fire chimed out nine o'clock as Anna and Natalie returned from the kitchen.

"What's wrong with everyone?" she demanded. "We don't want Alexander to think about us this way."

She was interrupted by sudden shouts outside the house. Alexander jumped to the window again and looked toward the main street.

"The trucks are here!"

Anna steadied herself against the table. There was a loud knock on the door.

"Alexander! Alexander! We're leaving now! Come on!"

Stepan hurried and let the group of young men in. There were seven of them, and they were all dressed in their warmest clothing.

"Alexander," Vassily, the son of the postmaster, began, "we hate to stop your party, but the trucks just arrived, and we're leaving in a few minutes. You'll have to hurry. We're going to pick up more men in several other villages this morning."

Alexander raced past them and up the stairs. Anna fingered the new scarf nervously and turned to Stepan. They looked at each other speechlessly. In a few minutes Alexander entered the room again carrying a small canvas bag of his belongings. He walked over, put the scarf around his neck, and said, "Everyone will be there to see us off. You'd better dress warmly—the air is cold."

The rest of the family and Kolya put on their coats, and the two women tied large handkerchiefs around their heads. And at ten minutes past nine they were walking up the small dirt road towards the gathering of villagers on the main street. Petasha proudly wore his new boots and carried the small wooden gun.

The entire populace had gathered near the trucks, which

most of the men were busy inspecting. The women were huddled against the side of the post office as a protection against the icy wind. The Sumarakovs watched Alexander as he threw his pack into one of the trucks and came back to join them.

When the officers who drove the trucks returned from their hot coffee which the postmaster had had ready for them, there were many goodbyes and kisses, but no weeping. A few silent tears, but no weeping. Alexander sat in the back of the truck and waved silently to his family as the machines drove away. They waved back at him until the three colors of the scarf blurred and disappeared.

A few of Petasha's friends were admiring his new boots and gun when the crowd began to disperse. It was only nine thirty, and there was plenty of work to do. Kolya promised the Sumarakovs that he would come and visit them that evening, but there was work he had to do on his own little farm during the day.

Petasha returned to his mother's side and spoke softly. "Mother, Nitya says I am too old to be called 'Petasha'—he says you should call me 'Peter.' "

Kolya watched Anna's face. She was looking in the direction in which the trucks had gone.

"No, child," she answered softly, "you are not too old to be called 'Petasha.' You will be 'Peter' soon enough."

She took his hand and walked slowly toward their house. Kolya's eyes followed the small group; then he turned towards his own home. As he moved along the main street, he felt again the bitter coldness of the air. The sky seemed darker than it had been at seven o'clock. Kolya put his hands in his pockets and stared at the ground. Winter comes earlier every year, he thought.

"How Are You, Eddie?"

Margaret Throne

EDDIE was glad it was clear and warm. He let the screen door bang behind him and walked down the front walk to the white picket gate. Junior Backell was riding by on his bicycle. "Morning, Eddie. Nice morning, ain't it?"

"Hi," said Eddie, and watched the boy disappear around the corner. He continued to stand behind the gate. It was very warm and pleasant there in the June sun, and Eddie could tell by the feel that summer was here to stay. He could tell too because Mary had told him that it was all right for him to put on his summer trousers and his straw hat now. Yes, now it was really summer. That meant no more school, and Junior and all the others would be home all day, and they would laugh and talk with him. That was much better than the winter when Mary made him stay indoors in the big front room. All winter he would sit there, looking out at the people through the bay window. Some of the people would wave to him if he waved, and he liked that. But summer was much nicer. Mary always let him go for walks whenever he wanted. He always enjoyed the walks better than anything—that is almost always. That one time, he remembered, a fat boy had made fun of him. At first Eddie had thought the boy was trying to be friendly with him.

"Ma says you're almost fifty years old, Eddie," he had said.

"Yeah," Eddie had said, although he wasn't sure—forty-something, Mary had told him. Maybe that was near fifty, he had thought. Then he had noticed the boy staring at him.

"Gee whiz," he had said, "you're older than my pop, and you can't even read or write. You can't, can you, Eddie?" Eddie hadn't answered him and had started to walk away. But the boy had continued. "How come you got the mind of a kid, Eddie? How come you're like that?" he had yelled. Eddie remembered the boy's jeering face and curling mouth, and the way he had suddenly been filled with an awful rage at him. Without realizing it, he had turned and grabbed the boy by the shoulders. His hands had seemed almost electric once he had grasped his tormentor, and he had been unable to let go. He remembered the sudden strength that had filled him then and how he had shaken the boy until his body was limp. Someone had come then and had taken him home, and for a long time after that Mary had kept him inside—nearly that whole summer. It was only after he had promised never to act that way again that she had let him go out. That had been a long time ago, but at times Eddie would see the boy pass by, and he would remember. The boy's eyes would always grow large when he saw Eddie, and he would walk faster—all the time looking at the ground. Eddie's hands felt queer as he thought of it. They became wet with perspiration, and he rubbed them over his trousers.

"Morning, Eddie," called old Mrs. Walker from across the street.

"Hi," said Eddie, and then he remembered that Mary had told him not to say that. She had told him for a long time, but somehow he always forgot. He could never seem to remember what it was he was supposed to say instead, and so he just went on saying "hi" to everyone who greeted him. Nobody seemed to mind. They always smiled back at him. Mary must be wrong, he thought.

He saw Mr. Drigger, the postman, coming up the street. Mr. Drigger was bent over under a heavy bag full of mail. He smiled as he saw Eddie. "How are you Eddie?" he said.

Eddie smiled back at him. He liked Mr. Drigger. "I'm good," he said, and after a moment's hesitation added, "How're you?"

"Fine, Eddie, fine," said Mr. Drigger. He was looking through some envelopes he had in his hand. "Got two letters here for your sister and a *Saturday Evening Post.*" He handed the letters and the magazine to Eddie and went on.

"Thanks," said Eddie.

"You bet," said Mr. Drigger, already going up the next-door walk.

Eddie started to take the mail directly in to Mary, but he stopped to look at the picture on the front of the magazine. It was of a girl with yellow hair putting flowers of various colors into a big blue vase. Eddie liked that. He always liked brightly colored things. He looked at the words under the picture, but they meant nothing to him. He was looking at the picture again when he heard the screen door open. It was Mary. He folded the magazine over the letters.

"Got the mail," he said, handing it to her. He noticed that she did not look completely happy.

"Thanks, Eddie," she said. "You forgot about going to Strand's for my groceries, didn't you?" Mary's voice was not angry, but Eddie felt ashamed. He always felt ashamed when he forgot, and he had tried so hard to remember.

"Oh," he said, digging the toe of his shoe into the soft dirt between the stones of the walk.

"It doesn't matter," Mary was saying; "you can go now. It's only nine thirty. Just try to be back by ten thirty." Eddie brightened. Mary never scolded him. She had taken care of him ever since he could remember, since he had been very young.

"Okay," he said, and again started down the walk and out through the picket gate. This time he'd remember sure. He didn't stop for anything after that until he reached the store. "Get the groceries," he kept repeating to himself the whole way, and he was very happy and a trifle proud when he found himself in Strand's Grocery.

He looked for Mr. Strand. He was the one who always gave Eddie Mary's order of groceries, but he couldn't see Mr. Strand anywhere. It was midmorning, and the little store was almost entirely filled with housewives who had waited until the last minute to buy their food for lunch. Eddie didn't like crowds. For a minute he thought he'd leave, but then he remembered Mary and decided to wait. For nearly ten minutes he stood patiently near the door. A few women had left, but more had come in. He still hadn't seen Mr. Strand. There seemed to be only Mrs. Strand and her son William waiting on all the customers. Mrs. Strand was spending most of her time conversing with her various friends. Eddie wondered why she didn't bother about all the people waiting there. He watched her as she talked. She had propped her fat white arms on the counter and was talking to a thin little woman Eddie had seen in the store before. He looked at Mrs. Strand's gray hair, the way some of it hung in strings around her balloon-like face and the way the rest of it was in tight little curls close to her head. He could hear her voice above all the others in the store. None of the others seemed to notice it, but Eddie knew he had to get away. He tried to move around so he would not hear it, but he could not find a spot in the room where he was not aware of its droning. Now and then it was broken by her harsh laugh. Again he thought of going, but again he remembered Mary and stayed. He couldn't help watching Mrs. Strand. Her glasses had slid half way down her nose, and she had made no effort to readjust them. Her long mouth was always opening and closing. Now she was reaching for a pretzel from a box which stood on the counter. She put the pretzel into her mouth and propped the fat white arm under her once more, never stopping her flow of chatter.

Eddie wanted more than anything to get out of the hot, stuffy store. There seemed to be more and more women coming, and he was still there at the door. No one seemed to notice him. Where was Mr. Strand? He felt confused and trapped. Mary wanted the groceries, but how could he get them? She had said by ten thirty, he remembered. What time was it now? There was a clock over the meat counter, but the numbers and the way the hands pointed meant nothing to him. He looked at the woman standing next to him. She was young, with black hair, and when she saw Eddie looking at her she smiled as though she knew him. He would ask her, he thought. She would tell him. She had turned her head away again, and Eddie tapped her timidly on the arm. "Hey," he said, "what time is it?" The woman looked at Eddie and then at the clock, which was directly facing him. For a moment he was afraid she would not answer him. "What time is it?" he asked again.

The woman seemed a trifle bewildered. "Why, it's ten after ten," she said uncertainly.

Eddie felt more panicky than ever. Ten after must be close to half past. He had to get the groceries and get out. He had to do something right for this once at least. Mrs. Strand was still talking. "Ten after," Eddie said to himself and began to shove his way through the crowd. He heard the indignant cries of women as he elbowed and tramped on toes, but he kept on going. He managed to get almost to the counter. He was close to Mrs. Strand now, and her voice was louder to his ears.

"So I told Harry," she was saying, "'Go right along with the fellas fishing. You need a rest,' I told him. 'William and me can take care of the store,' I sez. You know Harry," she went on; "he don't think nobody but him can do nothin' right. I told him three days ain't enough for us to ruin his store for him." She paused for breath. "You said you wanted a can of mushroom soup, didn't you?" she asked the woman to whom she had been speaking. Eddie saw the woman nod her head, but Mrs. Strand made no effort to move. "William," she said, "bring Mrs. Hubley a can of mushroom soup when you go to the back of the store."

Eddie looked at the little figure in the big white grocer's apron. William was hurrying back and forth, trying to wait on as many customers as possible. He always stopped and talked to Eddie on his way home from school. "Hi," Eddie called to him over the shoulder of the woman in front of him.

"Hi, Eddie," William said.

"Hurry, William," Mrs. Strand said. "Mrs. Hubley can't wait all day." Without a word William scurried to the back of the store.

"Fat, lazy woman," thought Eddie. "Ugly woman," he thought, and for a time he forgot everything but his growing hatred for the woman. He looked at the rolls of fat that made creases in her neck as she hunched over the counter. His hands were perspiring, and he rubbed them down over his trousers.

William came with the mushroom soup. "Here you are, Mrs. Hubley," said Mrs. Strand. "Nineteen cents." The woman gave her the money and turned from the counter to push her way to the door. Eddie was next to the counter now, directly in front of Mrs. Strand. His hands were perspiring more and more. He stood there staring at her. For a moment she stared back. Then she shrugged her shoulders and took another pretzel.

"Well, Eddie," she said, "what do you want? Speak up. Don't just stand there and stare like that. We're busy in here today."

"Hunh," said Eddie. "Oh, I want my sister's order—now."

At first she looked expressionless, as though she hadn't understood what he was saying. Then she winked at the woman standing next to Eddie. "Your sister didn't phone in no order this week, Eddie," she said. "We ain't got no order for her." Then she turned to the woman again, as though Eddie weren't even there. "Lord, we're so busy as it is, I don't see how people can expect us to fill phone orders."

"She told me to get it," Eddie said. "I want it!"

"I told you, Eddie, we ain't got it."

Eddie felt his muscles tighten. He was breathing faster. He looked into the woman's large white face. "You gimme it!"

"Just a minute," Mrs. Strand said, and for the first time she straightened up, taking her fat arms off the counter. "Let's not get excited about this thing. After all, it ain't my fault if your sister didn't phone in no order."

"My sister did," said Eddie, rubbing his hands over his trousers. "I gotta get it. I told her." Mrs. Strand's mouth curled.

"It must run in the family," she said to the people in general. By this time most of the women were watching. "Your sister probably just thinks she phoned the order. Why don't you go home and tell her?"

"No," said Eddie, and slapped his hands down on the counter. He didn't want to, he told himself. He didn't want to. He thought of the fat boy. "You get it!" he said hoarsely and brought his face close to hers.

Mrs. Strand's eyes opened wider and her face became a trifle paler. "I told you, Eddie, go home! Get your order and then come back. God," she said to the onlookers in an attempt to regain some of her composure, "he's goin' completely off his nut!"

Eddie's whole body seemed to tremble, and he was unable to keep from lunging forward. He felt his fingers tighten around the soft, fleshy neck. His hands were electric, as on the fat boy's shoulders. He felt the terrible strength, like hot liquid in his veins, driving the surging fury to his head. He couldn't let go. The woman's face was white, and her eyes were bulging. "You," he said in almost a growl and shook her hard. Her glasses fell off and clattered to the floor. The little curls were bouncing crazily askew. There was confusion all about him. A woman screamed. Eddie did not let go.

"Call the police!" someone said.

"Stop him!" yelled another.

Someone was tugging on his arms, trying to drag him away, but his strength was too great.

"Hit him on the head," someone said. "Knock him out!"

He saw only the white face and great terrified eyes.

"Stop it, Eddie," he heard. "Stop it!" The voice was crying and pleading, and for the first time Eddie turned his stare from Mrs. Strand's face. He saw William. He saw that his face was red and streaked with tears, and he felt him tugging and punching him. William, his friend, punching him. Eddie's hands relaxed and fell to the counter.

"Whatsamatter, William," Eddie said, "whatsamatter?" But William was paying no attention to him. He was helping his mother to a stool behind the counter.

"Ma," he was almost sobbing, "Ma, are you all right?"

"Get some water!" one woman said.

"Call a doctor!" said another.

They were crowding around Mrs. Strand. "She should have air," somebody remembered.

Eddie stood there staring at all the excited women. He heard only bits of their exclamations.

"He's a maniac," one was saying. "Somebody call the police!" Some of the women turned to look at Eddie. They seemed to be frightened of him, and none of them would venture to approach him. He stepped backward a few steps as if trying to decide what to do and then wheeled and ran as fast as he was able out of the store.

He ran for nearly two blocks, and then, being winded, he stopped and sat panting on the curb. There was no one coming after him. He would hurry right home, he thought. He got up, brushed his trousers, and started down the street. Mary would wonder where he had been. It must be after ten thirty now. Would someone tell her? He couldn't stay in the house all summer again. He couldn't. He stopped momentarily to look at a big yellow and green caterpillar on the trunk of a tree. He watched it crawl briefly and then sent it flying with a flip of his finger.

"Whatcha doin', Eddie?" came the voice from the street. It was Junior Backell going by on his bicycle again.

"Nothin'," said Eddie. "Nothin'. I didn't do nothin'." But Junior was already halfway down the block.

"Ugly fat woman," Eddie said to himself and went on down the street.

Woman's Whole Existence

Elinor Douglass

ALTHOUGH I know the imputation that lies over folk who go walking in graveyards at night, I must confess a liking for that very thing. The old cemetery is almost the only place in our village where one can get any thinking done. Quiet and apart, it slopes up a knoll, a place of grassy mounds and sinking stones with half-obliterated inscriptions: To Hannah, pious and virtuous relict of Tobias Wheeler, 1753. . . . Here lyeth Primaeus, a free Negro and a devoted servant, 1701. . . . To the memory of my beloved son who was lost at sea, 1813. Like all cemeteries it is a place of sorrow, but old sorrow, old regret, for the mourners have long ago followed the mourned, and they too lie forgotten. Whatever dreadful happened there, happened long ago. One cannot say as much for the village, where one may be shocked and frightened a dozen times in an hour.

So, at the risk of being called morbid, I will say that

some of my pleasantest hours have been passed leaning against an ancient stone, watching the moon rise over the river or listening to the soughing of the tamarack trees at the crest of the hill, dark and somber trees well befitting the place of death. I have found quiet and peace there, and once I met with an unusual adventure.

It was a dark and misty night when I climbed the hill, hoping for nothing more interesting than a glimpse of the lights of Glastonbury reflected in the black water of the river. There was no moon, no hope of a moon. I stopped by the Melbourne tomb and lit a cigarette. Then as I flipped away the match, I saw a figure seated on a headstone just before me.

"Oh, I beg your pardon," I said, thinking I had disturbed someone who had come to be alone.

The slight gray figure turned and answered in a voice hardly more than a whisper, "Oh, no, don't mind me; I only haunt this place."

Haunt! The very word sent a chill through me. I looked around, fearing that I should see a specter by every tombstone. The gray person interpreted my apprehensive glance. "Don't worry," she said; "they're all asleep long ago. No one troubles to haunt this place but me. I wouldn't if I could sleep, but I can't; I don't believe I ever shall sleep." She hid her face in her ghostly hands. To meet an ordinary ghost is one thing, but to meet one small and lonely who cries to herself is another. I felt my fear give way to curiosity, and emboldened by the lighted tip of my cigarette, which glowed comfortingly in the dark, I waited for her to speak.

At last she looked up, pulled her shawl over her shoulders, and twitched the folds of her billowy skirt as if to shake the tears from her. "I used to live in the village," she said, "in the Brooks house down at the Cove. Do you know it?" I knew it, an old sagging house with broken windowpanes and hanging blinds. The boughs of a lilac tree had grown across the door, as if forbidding anyone to enter and disturb its memories. Beautiful it might have been, but now—

She seemed to read my thought. "Distressing, isn't it? I can't bear to go down there any more."

"Even so," I said, "I should think you would rather go home than stay here."

She cupped her chin in her hand and looked at me gravely, as if she were wondering if I could be trusted. Then she spoke: "Only one place is home to me, and I can't go there because he doesn't want me."

"Oh."

"He lived with the Barretts on Maiden Lane—he was their cousin, and just back from the war. I can well remember how he used to sit in our drawing room and tell us how the British burned Washington. Althea and I used to creep under the spinet, we were so frightened. But I loved him even then, and when I grew older I—couldn't get over it, but he never knew it at all."

"But how could you—? Why didn't he—?"

She shrugged her shoulders. "He didn't guess. He didn't know that I used to run to the window to see him ride up the street on his black horse. He never saw me glance at him over my hymnbook at church. He never knew that it hurt me to see him walking afternoons with Olivia Villiers. French, she was—I used to look in my mirror at night and despair, for I knew I'd never have rosy cheeks, and curly black hair, and jet black eyes like Olivia's.

"He didn't know, and I couldn't tell him. I was alone with him just once in my life."

"What did he say, do you remember?"

"I've been remembering for over a hundred years, my dear. It was a day in February, and he had ridden over to borrow a book from my father. We were standing before the fireplace, he and I, and he smiled and said, 'I think we'll have an early spring,' and poked the fire. There was he, ready with a smile and a word for someone whom he thought of only as the daughter of an old friend; and I curtseyed, a model of propriety, and not daring to look at his face, I fixed my eyes on his cuff, or the brass buttons of his coat. Sometimes my glance would fall on his hands, and I would tremble when I thought what they could mean to me."

She clenched the tombstone and leaned towards me. "I tell you I was glad when I died, for then I was free. I went to the Barrett house nights and watched him through his study window. He'd try to read, or write; then a restless fit would seize him, and he'd take his hat and go off to see Olivia. But one night the window was open, and I slipped into the room. He was sharpening a quill, and the candle flickered shadows across his face. I hovered over his chair and kissed his eyes and mouth. I ran my fingers through his hair, and I was content. But he was not. He shuddered at my touch and scowled. He even cursed about the draft and got up to close the window. I was there before him. I ran out into the night. I heard him draw the bolt and knew I was locked out for all my death as I had been all my life."

"And you never went back?"

"I never went to the house again, but in spite of myself I used to haunt the garden. It was no good. He didn't want me living or dead." The thought overwhelmed her; again she started to cry.

I didn't know just what to do. One cannot slap a ghost on the shoulder and tell her to buck up. I waited discreetly, and then tried a little criticism. "It seems to me," I said, "that your attitude has been all wrong. You would have been justified if you'd caused him a little discomfort after all the pain he gave you. If I'd been in your place, I wouldn't have moved into the garden. I would have waited around until he went walking and then pushed his hat off. I would have gone into his study and hidden his ink, messed up the papers on his desk; and every time he kissed Olivia Villiers I would have pulled his hair."

The little ghost rose quickly and almost ran from me. "Oh, you don't understand!" she cried.

But I did.

In Flight

Theron H. Brown, III

In flight I seek and find fair Heaven's prize,
As free of care I skim the earth below,
And speeding, darting, playing, learn to know
The freedom God created in the skies.
Scenes only Heaven yields can thrill these eyes
Which from on high have seen the sunset's glow,
The birth of stars and planets row on row,
And beauties God to earth-bound man denies.
For I have lived with birds and clouds and stars,
And shared the secrets known to air-born things,
Soared far beyond the hold of man-made bars,
And felt vast power surging through my wings.
In flight I have transcended man's estate,
And found through space a path to Heaven's Gate.

[South Pacific, Summer, 1943]

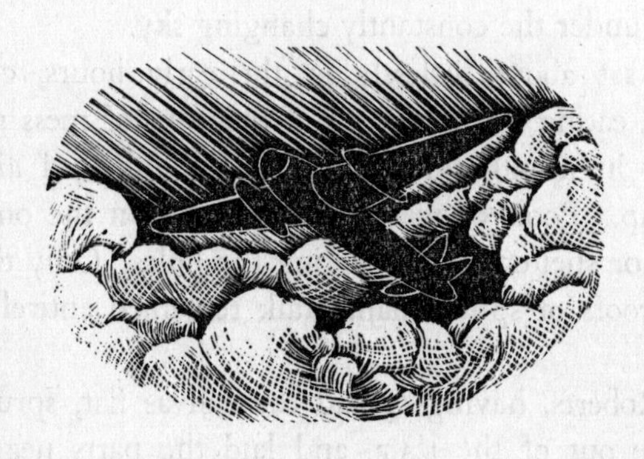

Beer for Christmas

H. P. Koenig

TO THE FRONT beyond the sandbagged holes barbed wire showed in thin strands against the dense undergrowth. There were no coconut palms in neat rows here. Just the obscurity of the low brush and leafed vines hanging down to the flanged roots of banyan trees. Farther out through bits of clearing the mountains started, monotonously green under the constantly changing sky.

Men sat about listlessly in the early hours, cleaning weapons, eating last remnants of food out of mess gear, or absorbed in month-old mail. The ground and air were still damp. Pools of water had collected in the once taut ponchos or shelterhalves covering the holes. Only the low, sloping roofs of split banana stalk remained entirely functional.

Sid Roberts, having spread the canvas flat, sprung the magazine out of the B.A.R. and laid the parts neatly side by side. It was a process that had long since become automatic. The trigger guard went next to the trigger-guard retaining pin, and the recoil-spring guide and recoil spring came after that, and so on up the line, and later they worked back in reverse order. Sometime they chanted the names of the parts softly to an old Fats Waller tune as they broke the weapons down, but some of the humor had gone out of the situation.

"Nothing you can do about the rust," Sid Roberts said, holding the operating handle up for Lefty to see. There were thin streaks of red along the outside.

Lefty didn't look up.

"A revolver's the only thing that'll stand up out here," Lefty said. "But even there the bluing comes off after a while."

Lefty shook various bits of cleaning gear out of a cracked waterproof bag. He threaded a patch into the end of the rod and then slipped the bolt out of the receiver.

"I didn't know what was coming off this morning," he said. "I thought I was cracking up. I felt the ground trembling and thought at first it must be the 155's landing in close, and then the whole earth started to rock, and I could see the trees shaking outside."

"Christ, on top of everything else, now earthquakes. Maybe the volcano's going to erupt."

"That would make this complete, wouldn't it?"

"Maybe that was the surprise Radio Tokyo promised us for Christmas."

Sid took the rod up and ran it through the bore. He looked down the muzzle.

"I think they were just bluffing, though," he went on.

"Like the time they said there wouldn't be a man alive on Code after September first."

Tompkins, the platoon runner, came across the clearing. He wore one-piece Navy coveralls and an automatic in a shoulder holster, and a wicked-looking Imperial saber hung from his belt. He stood at the edge of the clearing, flashing several books with brightly colored covers. With him was the corpsman.

"What you got there?" Lefty asked him.

"Mysteries," Tompkins said, holding the books up. "I just stole them from the Army."

Tompkins and the corpsman sat down on an empty wire drum.

"I just got the hot dope," Tompkins told them. "We're getting beer today."

"Yeah. And watermelon and ice cream." Lefty smiled at him pitifully and went back to cleaning the .03.

"No. This is straight. I just got it from a Seabee. He was down the beach and saw them unloading it from LST's."

"Sure. Seabees and the galley crews always get the straight dope." Sid laughed. "I know."

"Would that sound right, bringing beer in when chow and ammo have all priority?" Lefty asked them.

"I don't know, but that's what he said."

"It's probably for the Army," the corpsman said. "I've got a life-size picture of us getting beer, even if it is Christmas."

For a time they were silent. Lefty worked the bolt of the .03 a number of times and then snapped the trigger. Finally he pressed a clip into the receiver and stood the piece against a tree. Overhead now they could hear the swift flight of artillery shells and the percussion far out ahead. For a period of minutes there was a heavy concentration, and then the firing slacked off into intermittent bursts.

"Must be something big out there," Sid Roberts said. "It's been going on like that all morning."

"The lieutenant's got a patrol out now," Tompkins told them. "They should be coming in pretty soon. We'll find out then."

Suddenly Lefty stood up.

"I take it all back," he said. "But I wouldn't have believed it unless I saw it myself."

Back across the clearing where the C.P. was, men were stacking the flat cardboard cartons with the unmistakable white revenue stamps on them beside the tent. The word got around quickly. Already men were standing about watching the procedure speculatively.

Tompkins got up and crossed the clearing. They watched him join the group about the tent, and later he came back carrying a case.

"I've got yours here," he said.

They eyed the shining cans suspiciously. Sid Roberts built stacks with his, first trying two cans for a base and balancing two, one on top of the other, above. But that didn't work, so he used a base of three with one as the tower.

"Aren't you going to drink yours?" Lefty asked him.

"No. I'm saving mine for tonight and then going to drink all four cans."

"The way I figure it, it tastes just as good now as later."

"Maybe. But it's a little like a celebration. We always made quite a fuss about Christmas at home."

"You argue about it," Tompkins said. He pushed a long sheath knife deep into the can and then caught the overflow before it ran down the side. He cut a triangle and then passed the knife.

"Sure you won't have one? Here, have a beer. We have it all the time. Every afternoon a truck comes up with iced beer, and they give us all we want. Every afternoon, I said. That's one of the nice things about fighting in the jungle."

"I can wait," Sid Roberts said.

Lefty slammed the knife a quick blow. The blade cut the rim and a neat fountain spread into the air.

"You know, if you don't want it, you can pass it to me," the corpsman said.

Lefty looked at him with blinking eyes. There were bits of sud running down his cheeks.

"I'd think you'd have enough with the medical alcohol."

The corpsman shrugged his shoulders.

"I just didn't want to see any going to waste."

"Just like home," Tompkins said, holding the can up.

Lefty watched him.

"Imagine getting back and walking up to a bar, running your hand along the polished wood, and ordering a beer, just like it was the most natural thing in the world," Lefty said. "Taking your time and having another if you wanted, or just letting it go because you could always come back later."

"We don't have any bars in my town," the corpsman said.

"Where the hell do you live?" Tompkins asked him.

"It's just a small place on the Mississippi."

"Well I know that's one place I wouldn't want to come from. No bars. What kind of a deal do you call that?"

"It's got other things."

"You better get in on this," Tompkins told Sid.

"Hell, I've gone this long without; I guess I can wait a few more hours."

"Tell you what," Lefty said. "We'll all save a can or two and have them with you tonight just before dark."

"Fine," Sid said. "I'd like that. We can make it a party."

"I'll get some chow," Tompkins said. "I don't know what it'll be, but I'll get something. You wait and see."

There was a sudden commotion across the clearing. Men were going in and out of the tent. Someone called Tompkins by name and Tompkins got up, and he too went into the tent. When he came back he had a slip of paper in his hand.

"All right," Sid said. "Tell us the good news."

"Patrol," Tompkins said. "They got some Nips cornered in a pocket behind 700A. That's what all the firing was about. You and Lefty go. Sergeant Stafford's taking it."

Lefty slipped into the camouflaged jacket. He attached grenades by their spoons to his belt.

"You might know. Just when things were going good."

Sid Roberts pulled on a soft visored cap. He dropped the cans of beer into his pack and tightened the straps.

He looked up at Tompkins.

"Don't get any ideas about these."

Tompkins laughed.

"You know me better than that."

"That's just what I mean."

For Tompkins it turned out a very good afternoon indeed. The ground was drying now, and a warm laziness was in the air. Tompkins sat back, resting against the sandbags. He spent an exciting afternoon following the deft moves of Perry Mason and Della Street, following them through the rushed episodes in a series of apartment houses and hotels and finally ending up in the courtroom, with Mason suave, calm, twisting the case unexpectedly his way. The few moments of tenderness at the end and a promise of more great things to come. Tompkins put the book down. Far out to the front was an occasional spray of automatic rifle fire and then silence again. Once it seemed like light mortars opening up, but Tompkins couldn't be sure.

Later, towards evening, he saw the patrol coming in. They stood in a small group outside the tent. The corpsman was there, bending down, holding the dangling rubber hose from a plasma bottle. Lefty stood back quietly, watching him, shaking his head. He came back across the clearing slowly, dropping the rifle in his hole.

"How'd you make out?" Tompkins asked him. "Did you get any?"

"You got a cigarette?" Lefty asked.

Tompkins shook one loose and held the pack out to him.

"What happened?" Tompkins wanted to know.

"Everything went along all right for a while," Lefty said. "We cut across the river and then skirted the hill without running into anything. There's a little hollow with a sort of wall around it. Sid went on up ahead, peering over the ledge. I guess at first he didn't see anything and started to lift himself over. Just about then a Nambu opened up and caught him across the chest. I don't think he'll make it. He got stitched all the way across. Stafford went around from behind, and he could see them. There were quite a few, all dug in in their little holes in the roots of trees. Jesus, those scrawny little yellow bastards."

Lefty stripped the wet jacket off. He stood there a moment, staring at the ground blankly.

Somewhere off to the right in the silence of approaching evening was singing. The forgotten words of childhood and green firs and white days. The voices carried in a low, clear harmony.

Tompkins watched Lefty pull the soaked boots off.

"You want a beer?" Tompkins asked him.

"I thought I'd want one when I got back," Lefty said. "But I guess it doesn't make much difference now. I'd just as soon let it go."

"That goes for me too," Tompkins said.

Out ahead now men were hanging ration cans with pebbles in them on the barbed wire. Others were fixing low trip wires to loose pins in grenades. Lefty watched them and then climbed down into his hole. A few of Sid's things were still on the ground, and he picked them up, opened Sid's pack and put them in. The four cans of beer were still there. Lefty put the pack aside and settled down for the night. Outside, from a distance, the voices still reached him as a vague reminder, but it had become after all just another day.

A Country Boy

John Schaffner

A country boy upon a tumbled wall
sits on his hands to keep them from his sight
to hold them from the fragile texture of the night
lest they should mar the delicate thing
by being open to the air.

The gentlest fingers would be clumsy
at the breast of spring.

A young boy's lips are light to drink
upon the throat of new imaginings
but not so light as these white petals falling—

For when a wind lifts all the apple trees
in passionate motion and the night
grows sudden white and hurting sweet
(and soft and gleaming are the flanks of spring)
a boy must start and run, and run a longer hill
than he can find in crazy flight
if he's to shake the darkness straining in him,
break the will in these new voices calling.

The Long Dark Road

William Styron

DEWEY LASSITER walked along the road slowly, the dust rising in little vaporous clouds around his bare feet. He stopped at intervals to roll up the wet ends of his overalls, which slipped down to his ankles every few steps. In the distance, not more than half a mile across the broad, flat Delta country, he could see the lights of the store glowing faintly. Dewey increased his pace, still pausing occasionally to adjust his pants leg.

It was getting darker now, the boy thought to himself. He'd better be getting home, or he'd catch it plenty from his mother.

"Maw's gonna whup me," he thought aloud. He was surprised at the sound of his voice.

"Maw's gonna whup me," he said again, louder. From a heavily clumped pine grove off to the right beyond the cotton he heard the echo, "—whup me!" He laughed.

He shouted, "Maw's gonna whup me!" And the echo came back as before—"gonna whup me!" Then he was silent. He had better hurry, he thought, or he really would catch it.

From somewhere there came the harsh, long call of a bluejay. The boy walked on.

* * * * *

Lassiter's General Merchandise was typical of the many small country stores which one sees in the South. Its clapboard front, begrimed with the dust of many storms, was partly shielded by a flimsy roof, which was supported by two splintered and blackened posts. Between the posts were two old-style gas pumps and a pump for kerosene. And beside the door was a battered bench, hollowed through use and stained gray with time, above which was the fly-specked window and the chipped lettering: "A. J. Lassiter, Gen'l M'd'se."

The bench was the focal point for all local social activity. Worn into its grain, impressed into its gray and solid planking, were the imprints of many an overalled rump, and in its splintered fibre were the memories of numberless afternoons devoted to talking and spitting and thinking.

A. J. himself was an immense, ruddy-faced man of about forty with flaming red hair. He had a coarse and broad face, full of robust good humor; and his monstrous, balloon-like body, which seemed to overflow his shirt and pants with a fleshy and Gargantuan enormousness, gave him an appearance of stout and amiable heartiness. But A. J.'s most startling characteristic was his laugh.

It was no ordinary laugh. It was something akin to an explosion. When A. J. was amused, his massive face would seem to widen perceptibly, and his mouth would break out into an enormous grin. For a brief moment there would be a suspenseful silence; then it would begin. From somewhere in the depths of his voluminous bulk would emanate a sort of wheezing groan which built up gradually until his whole ruddy face and the entire immensity of his frame was convulsed by latent tremblings and rumblings. And then, his head thrown back, mouth agape, and face constricted with mirth, he would eructate in an ear-splitting paroxysm of exuberant, uninhibited laughter. And minutes would pass before he had, with countless wheezes and renewed outbursts of jollity, regained his composure.

A. J. had a family. His wife Mamie had borne him two sons and a daughter. The girl, Louesta, was now nineteen and studying to be a nurse in Memphis. The boys were Roy, who was twenty, and Dewey, who was just going on fifteen.

Roy worked in a garage in Clarksdale, twenty miles up the river. A. J. had wanted him to stay home and help on the farm, but Roy had told the old man he would rather "get out on his own." Roy was big and heavy like his father, and rather stupid. His new-found independence in Clarksdale consisted mainly of fierce gin bouts with his friends and parties on the weekends with the whores in Memphis, and more gin.

* * * * *

Dewey opened the screen door and went into the store. It was eight o'clock. He could tell by the big clock with the Agrico sign on it. It said eight fifteen, but always ran a little fast. No one was in but the old man, who was cutting some cheese in the back.

"Hi, Paw," he said.

A. J. looked up. "Hello, son," he said, smiling his broad smile. "C'mon back."

The boy went back to the big square wooden table. It had always sort of excited him, that huge heavy piece of wood with its countless cleaver marks and its warm mixed smell of strong cheese and raw, bloody meat. It was a savage sort of feeling that the block aroused in him, a feeling faintly bringing to mind pictures of blood, gore, and guts, like the sacrificial altar of the Aztecs he had seen in a history book. But it reminded him, too, of good food, of thick steaks, tender chops, and of Sunday dinners.

The old man was cutting through a big waxed block of yellow cheese, cutting it in long, easy strokes so that uniformly shaped wedges fell at the edge of the knife.

"Where you been to, Dewey?" he asked.

"Been fishin' down to the branch."

"Ketch anything?"

"Naw, dad-dratted catfish pulled my line in. Los' my bait an' my hook, an' I slipped in too."

A. J. looked up and saw the boy's wet overalls. He chuckled. "That'll learn you. Cain't ketch no catfish with pork rind. Holts on too hard. Gotta use 'hoppers or redworms." He laughed silently, his great body heaving. "Fell in! That'll learn you. Who'd you go with?"

"Lynwood Huckins."

"Why, that's George Huckins's young'un, ain't it?"

"Yep."

"Did he tell you 'bout his paw ketchin' that nigger?"

"Yep."

"Reckon he's mighty proud."

"Yep, Linwood said they're goin' to lynch that nigger."

"Now, son, don't say that." His father's face had lost

its usual smile. "That nigger's gonna git a fair and square trial."

"Where's Maw?" the boy asked.

"She's up to the house. She's waitin' supper on you now. You better git up there or she'll whup you." He laughed. "You don't want to get whupped."

And he thought about his mother, how she hardly ever said anything when she was mad like that, except to say, "Fetch me a cane, Dewey." But then, it never hurt very much, and besides, the old man had told her that he thought Dewey was getting too old to be whipped. The old man was like that—easy-going—wouldn't even cuss a nigger. Anyhow, it wasn't how it hurt his tail; but it hurt his feelings more. She was getting easier on him now. Maybe he *was* getting old.

"Yer brother Roy called up," A. J. said. "Said he'd be here around nine o'clock."

The son of a bitch, Dewey thought, the son of a bitch. The boy had nothing but hate and loathing for his brother, and he'd admit it to anyone. His own flesh and blood, but he detested the very sight of him. And he'd be here tonight, his fat, pasty yellow face, and his bleary eyes, his smelly breath and dirty nails, and he'd talk about himself.

And he'd be mean and nasty, and probably drunk, and he'd cuss Dewey and make him miserable like he'd been doing ever since he could remember. His own flesh and blood.

And the old man was just crazy about him. It was "Roy this" and "Roy that" and "He's goin' to be a success in this gosh-dern world, mark me!" And all the time the son of a bitch was in Clarksdale drinking and laying out in the gutter all the time, and he'd come back to the store about once a month, and all you'd hear was talk about how drunk he was last Saturday in Memphis and how much tail he got that night. Then he'd make Dewey run up to the bootleggers at Injun Mound and get him some whiskey and wouldn't give him anything except maybe a dime. The son of a bitch.

* * * * *

His mother hadn't whipped him, so Dewey felt relieved after supper. It was dark when he went back down to the store, which was connected with the house by a narrow path some eighty yards through the cotton field. From the back of the store he could see Nate Smith's battered old Ford under the dusty glare of the lights, and he knew that Nate and the old man would be out front on the bench talking.

He heard them as he rounded the corner of the store.

". . . and if'n I had my way, A. J., I'd take that black bastard and rope 'im to the highest tree in Mississippi!"

Dewey sat down on the strip of concrete near the pump and across from the two men. He listened, feeling the sand cool and brittle between his toes.

"Well, I wouldn't be saying anything as rash as that, Nate." His father's voice was low and steady and rich. "As I sees it," he said, with a trace of a smile playing around the corners of his wide mouth, "as I sees it, the State is the decidin' thing in all such matters of justice. When the prosecutor and the judge is elected by the people, the people is supposed to back up their decisions, and as I sees it, after they says their decisions, the people should let well enough alone."

But Nate was vehement in his convictions, "I know, I know, but goddamit—" His face was dead set, earnest. "All right, let's look at it like this. Suppose you was ol' man

Hooker. He was crippled up, almost helpless, A. J.; you know that yourself. All right. You're sleepin' over your store one night peaceful-like. Suddenly you wake up and hear somethin' creepin' around. You're helpless now, A. J., and you're all alone. You holler, 'Who's there?' and then you see somethin' like an ape over your bed, and he's stranglin' you with his big, black, common nigger hands! Why, goddamit, A. J., John Hooker didn't have no more strength than a baby. How can you sit there—" He stopped, breathing hard, and his lean, wrinkled face was a mixed study of anger and overworked imagination.

A. J. was calm and reassuring. He placed his fat hands on Nate's knee comfortingly.

"I know, I know," he said softly; "calm yourself now, Nate; there ain't no use gittin' so riled. The way it looks to me is that nigger is safe behind the bars up to Injun Mound, and there ain't nothin' me and you can do but let justice go its way and—"

"Yes, but goddamit, he was a nigger, a black, common, dirty son of a bitch of a nigger, and—"

"Sure, sure, it was a pretty terrible thing to do, I'll admit, even for a white man, let alone a nigger; but there just ain't one thing we can do. Let's just forget about it an' have a drink."

He looked at Dewey, and the boy knew what to do. Dewey went into the store and got three coca-colas out of the drink case and brought them out and gave one to the old man and one to Nate. Then he went over and sat down again on the concrete steps.

He took a swallow of the coca-cola, and it tasted good. And then he suddenly became aware of something. It was something he could not place exactly; but there was a certain feeling that made him uneasy. It was not a feeling that something was wrong; but he was conscious of the fact that there should be something there that wasn't. Something vital in the atmosphere was missing. He couldn't place it.

The air was hot and sultry, and he could smell the loamy, heavy odor of the Delta soil. He heard the steady drone of the flies and there was still the distant piping song of the frogs. A grasshopper spanked up against the screen and clung there momentarily, then buzzed away. From across the field he could hear the sudden, haunting, echoed call of a whippoorwill. A car passed on the road.

They were all there. But something was the matter.

"Yes, A. J.," he heard Nate say in his halting, cracked voice, "I ain't as spry as I used to be. Ol' Doc Barham up in Memphis says its dia-bee-tees. Cain't travel much. Like to come up here and talk with the boys, though."

The boys, the boys. That was it. Where were they? Monroe Davis and Charley Cutchin and Dexter Capps and all the rest. It wasn't right. Something was missing.

And then the horrible thought struck him, smote him with the jolt of a two-ton tractor. It was a lynching party. That's what Lynwood Huckins had said, had said that all those friends of his old man and old Huck himself were going up to Injun Mound and break that jail and get that nigger out of there and string him up; it was a secret. It was a secret. They were going to take him and string him up.

And then a strange feeling of unutterable terror came over the boy. He was afraid, but he could not comprehend his fear. He was conscious of strange, benumbing reality, knowing that somewhere not far away something inhuman and terrible and brutal was happening. It was fierce, unbelievable, untrue. But the incredible thing was there; and time passed slowly as he sat there, dazed, listening blankly to the drone of the two men's voices and the steady thrumming of the flies and the slow, interminable ticking of the clock.

Then suddenly he heard the faint sound of a car horn far down the road. It shocked him suddenly and hard. For the sound, as slight and noiseless as it really was, like the soft rustling of a mouse in the moldering antiquity of a forgotten attic, was to him as enormous and as frightening as the report of a cannon.

And now, above the sound of a horn, which was blowing continuously, he could hear the staccato clacking of a cutout on a high-powered engine. It was Roy. Dewey looked at the clock. Nine thirty.

The car, wheeling and lurching off the dusty road, came to a jarring halt in front of the store. The men, who until then had been obviously lost in the meanderings of their conversation, looked up in gaped-mouth astonishment at the car. Then the old man recognized his son and got up heavily and rose to greet him.

"Ho, Roy. Where you been?"

The youth did not answer his father, but leaned a drunken, leering face out of the window and began to laugh. It was startling to Dewey, and there was something hideous and obscene in the laughter. It was a ghastly and fiendish travesty on the laughter of his father, which, coming now with no apparent cause or reason and lacking any of the good-natured robustness of his father's laugh, seemed to echo a sound of loathesome and sickening bastardy in its foul coarseness.

Then he stopped suddenly and turned his drowned eyes on the startled people.

"They're bringin' that nigger up here."

The old man stared at his son, and then, as if the full but yet incomprehensible horror had dawned upon him, he leaped to the window.

"What you talkin' about, Roy? What nigger?" His words were almost savage, but they were the words of a man who has just been stricken by some nameless fear and, instead of planning escape, attempts to cover his terror with disbelief.

"What's the matter with you?" he cried, his huge body trembling with each gasping breath. "What nigger you talkin' about?"

"You know what nigger I'm talkin' 'bout," Roy said drunkenly. "They done sprung that nigger from jail. Dexter Capps and Charley Cutchin and a big bunch of them. They're bringin' him up here!" And then, with a sodden leer, he said, slowly and thickly, "They're goin' to burn him."

The old man stood there clutching the side of the door so that the backs of his hands were white. His voice was a whisper as he spoke to Roy.

"It ain't goin' to happen. So help me God! It ain't goin' to happen."

Just then Nate, who had been listening intently to all that had taken place, gave a sudden yell. "Listen! Listen! They're comin'!"

And they turned their eyes to the south, down the dark road. Dewey could see, not far away, a white glare of headlights; and he heard the jumbled noise of many cars, going fast, as they sped in a whirl of dust down the road.

The cars, drawn up in caravan fashion and numbering perhaps ten, stopped on the opposite side of the road. Each one was packed with five or six farmers. The men got out of the cars and walked over in front of the store and stood there, muttering in little angry groups and smoking and spitting and waiting.

Dewey heard his father talking. "What you all come out here for? I don't want any . . ."

"Look, A. J.," It was Jim Bickford's voice. "We had to bring him out here to git away from town. Anyhow," he said meaningfully, "there's kerosene out here."

"But hang it all, Jim, I don't want . . ."

Then Dewey heard his brother. "Here comes the truck! Here comes the truck! Hot damn!" He had staggered out of the car and was standing in the middle of the road, reeling and shouting and laughing like an idiot.

The son of a bitch, Dewey thought, the son of a bitch.

The truck, a huge hay wagon with slatted sides, stopped noisily in front of the store. The crowd of men gathered around it.

"Bring the bastard out of there!" someone shouted.

"Get that rope!"

Two men moved toward the store.

The old man lumbered over to the door. "Stop it now," he panted. "It's wrong!" His huge face was contorted and red. "Stop it—"

The men brushed him aside. "Git out of the way, A. J.," they said.

The two beefy farmers who had been in the truck got out. Between them, almost slumped to the ground, was the nigger. He was thin and short, so small that he looked like a dwarf beside his captors. Dewey could not see his face, but he could hear him. He was moaning. It was like nothing the boy had ever heard. It was something like the thin, piteous cry of a dog that has been caught in a steel trap; and yet it was something like the stricken wail of a woman, something mournful, terrible, and lost.

The two farmers pushed their way through the crowd, dragging the nigger between them. "This'll be all right," one of them said.

They pushed the nigger down on the steps, and he slumped lifelessly against the screen door, sweating, his eyes closed, still moaning.

Then Charley Cutchin stepped up beside the nigger and, grasping his collar, jerked him up. Charley was a tall and skinny man, thin almost to the point of emaciation. He wore steel-rimmed glasses and his eyes were bloodshot.

"Listen, nigger, you know what we're goin' to do?"

The nigger opened his eyes and looked at the cadaverous figure swaying before him. The white-shirted men had crowded around the door and were gathered there in a sweating mass beneath the lights, muttering and shuffling nervously.

"I tell you what we're goin' to do," he said, in a low voice; "we're goin' to hang you by your goddam black nigger neck. And then," he whispered, pointing to the gas pump, "we're goin' to burn you."

The nigger slumped back against the door, his hands in front of his face. And then he began to speak for the first time. He was sobbing now; the words came hoarsely.

"Don' burn me, suh; don' burn me."

Roy pushed through the crowd and lurched toward Charley.

"Let's get started, Cutchin; the police might be comin'."

"Yeah," said Charley, "let's get started."

The men moved back again toward the road, and six of the farmers grabbed the nigger. The nigger had now collapsed, and he shuddered as they dragged him over beneath the rafters. Roy, who had been holding the rope, threw the looped end around the nigger's neck and jerked it roughly. A little grazed, bloody patch showed where the fiber of the rope had scraped the skin.

Charley grasped Roy's arm.

"Take it easy, goddamit; we don't want to do it too soon!" He turned to Jim Bickford. "Get the truck."

Dewey saw them bring the truck up and back it up to within a few feet of the nigger, who had now fainted away completely and was being held up by Charley. A young boy had climbed a ladder and was tying the free end of the rope to a rafter which supported the roof.

And Dewey saw the crowd of men, perspiring, red-faced, and silent, who now stood as a mass, motionless, at the edge of the road. Hardly a word was spoken. They watched and remained silent. Dewey could hear only the steady thrum of the night flies, and the low muttering of the little group of men who stood around the nigger, intent, nervous, quiet. The old man was sitting on the bench alone with his head in his hands, rocking back and forth, and saying: "Oh, Jesus, oh, my sweet Jesus."

Charley, with Nate and Bickford, picked up the nigger, the rope still tied around his neck, and put him in the back of the truck. There was a dull thump as they dropped him in a lifeless heap on the planking.

Jim kicked him, kicked him hard, so that he sprawled out on the floor of the truck.

"Wake up, nigger," he said.

But the nigger would not move.

Roy shouted to the three men on the truck. "Throw some kerosene on the son of a bitch. That'll fix him!"

Someone handed a can of kerosene to Charley. Charley unscrewed the top and threw the contents into the nigger's face. The kerosene soaked into his clothes and dripped down on the floor of the truck. The nigger woke up and began to scream, awfully, hoarsely, and like a woman. The kerosene glistened on his black face.

"Don' burn me!" he screamed, "Oh Lord, don' burn me!"

Charley knocked him down with the kerosene can. The nigger, stunned, lay on the floor, sobbing and moaning.

Someone shouted from the road. "Let's get it over with, Cutchin!"

Dewey saw the three men jump down from the truck. Roy reeled into the driver's seat and started the motor. There was a tremendous roar, and a blue burst of flame exploded from the exhaust. Over all there was the heavy odor of kerosene, and the terrible moaning of the black figure in the back of the truck. The nigger got up and began to hold on to the slatted sides of the truck. He was screaming again, screaming in a high-pitched wail that echoed above the sound of the motor into the stillness of the night.

"Let 'er go, Roy," Charley shouted.

Dewey saw the truck lurch forward. There was a grinding of rubber against the gravel. The nigger's hands were torn loose from the palings as the rope drew tight around his neck and stifled his screams. He skidded sideways across the floor of the truck as the machine tore from beneath him. There was a heavy jolt, and a crack of loosening timbers. The body swung gently beneath the rafters.

Dewey was running, running across the cotton fields, and he could feel the clumps of earth between his toes and there was a smell of kerosene still in his nostrils . . . running, running, running. . . .

Running. And the great forest loomed far and away. For there was somewhere the smell of kerosene and sweat and burning flesh. Far and away. And beyond the fields of cotton there was a great forest. Far and away, Dewey, far and away. The tears stung his eyes, his eyes, Dewey, far and away. And running through the fields where the brambles are and the sound of a lark, Dewey, far and away. And running from death and burning niggers and Roy Roy Roy son of a bitch sooo-o-o far and away. The old man's laugh sitting with head in hands and the smell of kerosene, Dewey, Dewey, Dewey, Dewey, it is me, me me, Dewey, me doan' burn *me* suh like a woman. Late late in the evening and the hounds are calling; somewhere the river flows far and away. Oh my Jesus my sweet Jesus and murmuring voices far and away.

In the distance a train whistle blew, wailing up through the valley. All was quiet.

Snow in the Morning

Frances Gray Patton

The giant pine looks down on the snowy morning.
Remember? That is how the mind once stood,
Somber with the elation of discovery,
Like the tallest pine in the wood.

The wind has shaken and polished his lofty branches,
And dark above the snow be-clouded pines,
He observes the intricate streams map out a white country
In black, definitive lines.

How cold and cleansing were those currents of air
In our illumined morning, long ago;
How certain and lovely the winding of the waters
Upon that ephemeral snow.

Winter Night

Frances Gray Patton

The moon-pale night was quiet with a deep
And moving stillness; from the frozen ground
Tree shadows struck out music that did sweep
With one wide stroke the air all clean of sound.
The round moon and the stars dimmed by her light,
The one transparent line of cloud, bare trees—
Each lost its separate beauty to the night,
Became a note in ordered cadences.
It was a night to clear the mind of pain,
Steady the heart, and tranquilize the eye,
Draw fancy homeward from its wanderings far,
Temper the fires that danced along the vein—
Then, silenter than the silence, leapt a star
Like a white piece of crystal from the sky.

In Common with the Earth

Frances Gray Patton

In common with the Earth, the mind has weather—
Puts forth its tentative leaf, sets fruit, is lost
In birdless wastes where even the lovely voices
Of running waters fail before the frost:

But with a difference, that the Earth remembers
Blossom and snow, imagines nothing strange,
Turns white, turns green, but turns at ease, considering
How the one law unchangeable is change.

This human mind, alone, is non-retentive,
The victim of its own immediate breath;
Its winter woods weep: "Summer was a fable!"
Its twig in bud declares: "There is no death!"

Contributors

Theron H. Brown, III (A.B., '39), graduate of the East Orange High School, New Jersey, was an economics major in college and captain of the cheer leaders. He was Honor Man in his class at the Naval Reserve Air Base in Atlanta, December, 1941, and was a captain in the Marine Air Corps when he met his death in action, Solomon Islands, September 12, 1943. Shortly before his death he was awarded the Air Medal with Presidential Citation and, after it, the Purple Heart. The Marine Corps will publish a small volume of his verse.

David Cornel DeJong, who came to this country from the Netherlands, is a graduate of Calvin College, Grand Rapids, Michigan. He was awarded his master's degree at Duke in 1932 on the thesis "Some Aspects of the Modern Short Story with Original Examples." He is the author of several novels: *Belly Fulla Straw* (1932), *Old Haven* (1938), *Light Sons and Dark* (1940), *Day of the Trumpet* (1941), and *Benefit Street* (1942). *Across the Board*, his collected verse, appeared in 1943. The following year Houghton-Mifflin gave him a prize of $1,000 for his autobiography, *With a Dutch Accent*. His short stories have appeared from time to time in the annual collections. "Calves" won third prize, for instance, in the *O. Henry Memorial Prize Stories* for 1939. DeJong devotes his entire time to writing and lives in Providence in the winter and in West Barrington, Rhode Island, in the summer.

ELINOR DOUGLASS (A.B., '34) came to college from Northfield School for Girls, Massachusetts. She read for honors in English literature, was graduated *magna cum laude*, and is a member of the Phi Beta Kappa Society. She teaches English at Hood College, Frederick, Maryland.

LORENZ EITNER (A.B., '40) was born in Bruenn, Czechoslovakia, and lived there and in Austria, Germany, and Belgium before coming to America in 1935. He entered college from the high school at Florence, South Carolina. He read for honors in English literature, edited the *Archive*, was elected to Phi Beta Kappa, and was graduated *summa cum laude*. He completed his work for the doctorate in the history of art at Princeton in 1943. He is a second lieutenant, Office of Strategic Services, in the American Army of Occupation, Austria.

CREIGHTON GILBERT, the son of Professors Allan and Katharine Gilbert of the University faculty, entered college from Miss Barry's Foreign School, Florence, Italy. He remained at Duke three semesters, 1938-40. Within the year he expects to finish his doctoral dissertation at New York University on sixteenth-century Italian theories of painting. He has published three articles in learned journals. His translation of Michelangelo's sonnets and madrigals is to be issued by the Cummington Press.

EDGAR C. GREENE, a graduate of Southeastern High School, Detroit, dropped out of college at the end of his sophomore year (1940), spent two years in Mexico, and joined the Marine Corps in 1943. A second lieutenant attached to the Twenty-ninth Marines, he was severely wounded on Okinawa, May 17, 1945. His contribution to this volume won an Honorable Mention in the annual college contest run by *Story* (1940).

R. P. HARRISS (A.B., '26) entered Trinity College from

the Fayetteville High School. He was closely associated with the *Archive:* he won the Southgate Prize for the best short story one year, the Sigma Upsilon Prize for the best contribution the next. He edited the magazine and the *Archive Anthology* (1926), the first collection of Duke verse. Braithwaite ran his "September Transient" and two other poems in his *Anthology of Magazine Verse* in 1926. In the early thirties Harriss belonged to the staff of the New York *Herald* in Paris and while there studied at the Ecole d'art animalier. He has been an associate editor and Literary Editor of the Baltimore *Evening Sun* since 1934. He is the author of *The Foxes,* a novel of plantation life in the Cape Fear Country. The British Booksellers' Association awarded this volume the Cinderella Slipper for "the most deserving literary work of fiction published in England in 1937."

KIFFIN ROCKWELL HAYES (A.B., '39) attended the Asheville School for Boys before entering Duke. He was editor of the *Archive* in his senior year. During the war in Europe he was attached to Headquarters, Sixth Armored Division. On June 29, 1945, Hayes was decorated with the Bronze Star Medal for his "heroic service," his "devotion to duty and disregard for personal safety" while working with front-line troops of this division in its campaign across France, Belgium, Luxembourg, and Germany, November, 1944-March, 1945.

The late Lee Happ (A.B., '42), First Lieutenant, U.S.M.C.R., the subject of one of Hayes's poems, was posthumously awarded the Bronze Star Medal for his "indomitable spirit and steadfast devotion to duty in grave peril."

ELIZABETH DILTS KIBBEE (Mrs. Wallace G. Kibbee, Jr.), graduate of the Durham High School, spent two years (1940-42) at Duke, after which time she specialized in home economics at the Woman's College of the University of North Carolina. She lives in San Francisco, where she is an assistant editor of *Sunset Magazine.*

H. P. KOENIG (A.B., '41) is a graduate of the Curtis High School, Staten Island, New York. He was assistant editor of the *Archive* in 1940-41. He is a captain in the Marine Corps

Reserve and has seen action, among other places, at Guadalcanal and Bougainville.

Olive Sherertz Lanham (Mrs. C. W. Lanham, Jr.) prepared for college at the American School, Shanghai, China, and at the Durham High School. She belongs to the Class of 1946.

Harold Grier McCurdy (A.B., '30, Ph.D., '38) is Professor of Psychology and Philosophy at Meredith College, Raleigh. He entered Duke from the Boyden High School at Salisbury and was graduated Phi Beta Kappa and *magna cum laude*.

Kenneth Dougal McDougall (Ph.D., '42), the son of Mrs. Anne A. McDougall and the late Professor William McDougall, attended the Dragon School, Oxford, England, and Brown and Nichols' School, Cambridge, Massachusetts. He pursued a premedical course at Duke (1927-30). He continued his studies in Great Britain, first at the University of Reading, then at the Royal Dick Veterinary College, University of Edinburgh, where he was granted a diploma in 1934. He returned to Duke in 1938 for a doctorate in zoology. His dissertation was on *Sessile Marine Invertebrates of Beaufort, North Carolina.* McDougall was Angier Duke Fellow in 1941-42 and in that year was elected to Phi Sigma Biological Society, Sigma Xi, and Phi Beta Kappa. He served as a second lieutenant of infantry in the First Special Service Force, night fighters, with the Fifth Army in Italy and later with the Seventh Army in southern France. There on the night of September 15, 1944, he was killed in action, aged thirty-six, while leading a patrol into enemy territory. He was awarded, posthumously, the Purple Heart.

Ralph Nash received his high-school training at St. Petersburg, Florida, and was graduated from college, Phi Beta Kappa and *summa cum laude*, in 1945. In his junior year he won the Erasmus Club Prize for the best critical essay by an undergraduate. At present he is doing research on Ben Jonson in the Graduate School.

Frances Gray Patton (Mrs. Lewis Patton) entered Trinity College from the Newport News High Schol in 1922. During her year at Trinity she won the Sigma Upsilon Prize for the best contribution to the *Archive*. Thereafter she attended the University of North Carolina, where she was prominent in dramatics. Her story *A Piece of Bread* won Second Prize over 1,100 other entries in the annual *Kenyon Review* contest and appeared in that quarterly, autumn, 1944. It has been reprinted in this year's *O. Henry Memorial* volume. Mrs. Patton lives in Durham.

Ovid Williams Pierce (A.B., '32) lives in Weldon, where he went to the local school. He read for honors in English literature, was elected to Phi Beta Kappa, and was editor of the *Archive*. For two years he was a member of Robert Hillyer's composition class at Harvard. Martha Foley, editor of *The Best American Short Stories*, listed Pierce's "One of the Darkies" as being among the distinguished stories of 1943. He has been attached to Headquarters, Base Command, Trinidad, during the war.

Ethel Davis Ramsay (Mrs. William J. Ramsay) came to Trinity College from the Durham High School. She received her bachelor's degree in 1926 and her master's two years later. She was on the *Archive* staff and is a member of Phi Beta Kappa. Braithwaite included her "Esthetic Experience" and "Unrest" in his *Anthology of Magazine Verse* for 1926. Mrs. Ramsay lives near Kingsport, Tennessee.

Julian Lee Rayford came to college from the Ensley Howard High School, Ensley, Alabama, and remained at Duke for one year (1927-28). He has had a varied career as painter, poet, hobo, sculptor, lecturer, and originator of "chants" on Abe Lincoln, Davy Crockett, and other American heroes, real and imaginary. Rayford has given an account of his early life in the autobiographical novel *Cottonmouth* (1941). He lives in New York.

Mildred Stites Reed (Mrs. John F. Reed) came to Duke from Bethel Woman's College, Hopkinsville, Kentucky, in 1931. She was graduated, Phi Beta Kappa, two years later and took her master's degree in biology, 1935. During her senior year she edited the *Distaff*, Woman's College literary journal, now discontinued. She lives in Berea, Ohio.

ARCHIE ROBERTSON (A.M., '30) was a graduate student of English after taking his bachelor's degree at Harvard in 1928. He has been a journalist in Washington since 1934. He is the author of *The Government at Your Service* (1939) and of *Slow Train to Yesterday* (1945), an account of his travels on American narrow-gauge railways. During the war he served for a time in the Office of War Information in Cairo, Egypt.

MARY GUS RODGERS (MRS. WILLIAM H. SCHOEN, III) lives in Louisville, where she attended the Atherton High School for Girls. From time to time she has written feature articles for the *Courier-Journal*. She spent two years (1940-42) at Duke. She was graduated from the University of Chicago. *Charm* has published three of her stories during the current year.

JOHN SCHAFFNER received his A.B. degree, *cum honoribus*, from Bowdoin College in 1935 and at the same time won the literary award, The Henry W. Longfellow Graduate Scholarship. He spent a year as an advanced student of English at Duke. He was special rewrite man on the W.P.A. Writers' Project, *Maine: A Guide Down East* (1937). In the same year he published privately an early sheaf of poems called *An Island Boy*. Other poems have appeared in the *Saturday Review of Literature*, *Yankee*, *Voices*, *Tomorrow*, the *Fountain*, and *Harper's*. He served as an ensign, U.S.N.R., for one year but was honorably discharged on grounds of ill health. He lives in Springfield, Ohio, where he belongs to the editorial staff of *Collier's*.

ROBERT A. SCOTT, JR., attended the University of Virginia for a few months before coming to Duke with the Marine Unit in July, 1943. After three semesters he was assigned to the Marine Detachment on the aircraft carrier U.S.S. "Bunker Hill." He was aboard this vessel when it was hit by a Japanese plane off Okinawa, May, 1945.

HENRY A. SIMONS came to Duke from the Richmond Hill High School, New York, N. Y., and spent two years (1942-44) in college, during the last of which he belonged to the V-12 Unit. He took first honors in the U.S.N. Radio School, University of Wisconsin, before leaving for the Pacific in June, 1945, as a radio operator.

RICHARD AUSTIN SMITH, graduate of Mercersburg Academy, was editor of the *Archive* in his third and last year of college, 1933-34. He spent three years with the Department of Labor. In 1939 he joined the staff of *Think Magazine*, trade journal of the International Business Machines Corporation. Knopf brought out his novel *The Sun Dial* (1942), a chapter of which appears in this book. Smith enlisted in the Army in November, 1943, and was on the staff of the newspaper *Army Talks* in Paris when the European war ended. As a private, first class, he was appointed in June, 1945, an instructor in story writing at the Army University Center, Shrivenham, England.

WILLIAM H. SNITGER, III, attended the high school at Beaver, Pennsylvania, and entered Duke in 1941. He belonged to the N.R.O.T.C. and was commissioned an ensign in February, 1944. After being trained as a deep-sea diver, he was assigned to the U.S.S. ATR 57.

REBECCA KIRKPATRICK SPRINKLE (MRS. WILLIAM VAN E. SPRINKLE) entered Trinity College from the high school at Hickory. She is a Phi Beta Kappa graduate of the Class of 1928 and lives in Durham.

WILLIAM C. STYRON, JR., attended Christ Church School, Christ Church, Virginia, and Davidson College before joining the Marine Unit at Duke in July, 1943. He is at present in the Pacific Theater. His "Autumn" was awarded an Honorable Mention in the 1944 contest sponsored by *Story*.

VIRGINIA HODGES TABLER (MRS. EDWARD TABLER) of Charleston, West Virginia, prepared for college at the Shipley School, Bryn Mawr, Pennsylvania. She was on the *Archive* staff, read for honors in English literature, and was graduated, Phi Beta Kappa, in 1940.

DONALD THOMPSON, '46, came to Duke in the spring of 1944 from Tennessee Wesleyan College, Athens. He is in the N.R.O.T.C.

MARGARET THRONE, a graduate of the high school at York, Pennsylvania, belongs to the Class of 1947.

NEWMAN IVEY WHITE (A.B., '13, A.M., '14) is Chairman of the English Department. At Trinity College, which he entered from Greensboro High School, he was captain of the tennis team, editor of the *Chanticleer*, and first winner of the Sigma Upsilon Prize. He took his doctorate at Harvard. In his verse-writing class and out, he has been for many years the friendly critic of aspiring poets on the campus, many of whom are represented in this anthology. His scholarly interests have centered about folklore and the English romantic poets: he edited *An Anthology of Verse by American Negroes* (with W. C. Jackson, 1924), *American Negro Folk Songs* (1928), and is at the moment general editor of the Frank C. Brown Folklore Collection. He edited the *Best of Shelley* (1932) and traced the history of Shelley's reputation in *The Unextinguished Hearth* (1938). His monumental two-volume *Shelley* appeared in 1940, and an abridgment of this work, *Portrait of Shelley*, in 1945.

VERGIL WHITE is a pseudonym.

JAMES C. WICKSTROM, graduate of the Lyons Township High School, La Grange, Illinois, left college in the middle of his sophomore year (1943) to join the Army. He is a corporal, engaged in radio work in the South Pacific.

OPAL WINSTEAD entered Duke as a special student from Eastman College, Poughkeepsie, New York, in 1924. She was assistant editor of the *Archive*. Since leaving college she has been a free-lance writer in Charlotte.

FRANCES WRIGHT, graduate of the Phillips High School, Birmingham, Alabama, spent two years (1942-44) at Duke. She appeared in the Duke Players' production of *The Little Foxes* during her sophomore year.

GEORGE ZABRISKIE entered Duke from the high school at Caldwell, New Jersey, in 1937, but dropped out of college for two years before taking his degree in 1944. His first public recognition came in 1940 when Mount Holyoke College awarded him the Irene P. Glasscock Memorial Prize for poetry. The *Archive* published many of the poems which were to make up *The Mind's Geography* (1941). On the strength of this volume, Zabriskie was given a Guggenheim Fellowship in 1942-43. The fruit of this fellowship year, spent in Durham, is *Like the Root* (1945), a book illustrated by Zabriskie's wife, Elizabeth Capehart (-'42). He served as instructor in verse and modern poetry at Black Mountain College, North Carolina, for a year. He is now Poet in Residence at Marietta College, Marietta, Ohio. Mrs. Zabriskie is Artist in Residence at the same institution.

The following illustrated and designed the book under the direction of CLARE LEIGHTON: MARY DIMMITT, '47, of Swarthmore, Pennsylvania; LORING FOUNTAIN, '47, of Sherman Oaks, California; WINIFRED GRUBBS, '47, of Pittsburgh, Pennsylvania; MARGARET JENKINS, '46, of Salisbury; MARGARET JEAN MEEKER, '48, of East Orange, New Jersey; JANE MERIWETHER, '46, of Kansas City, Missouri; KATHRYN ANN MORRISON, '48, of St. Petersburg, Florida; JANE NOEL, '47, of Durham; JOSEPHINE ANNE PATY (A.B., '45), of Elizabethton, Tennessee; BARBARA PERKINS, '46, of Rutland, Vermont; JESSIE LOU VEREEN, '46, of Miami, Florida; ANN WILSON, of Durham; ANNE ZENER (MRS. KARL ZENER), of Durham.

appeared in the Duke Players' production of *The Little Foxes* during her sophomore year.

OSKAR ZATURENSKI entered Duke from the high school at Oakhurst, New Jersey in 1937, but dropped out of college for two years before taking his degree in 1942. His first public recognition came in 1940 when Mount Holyoke College awarded him the Irene P. Glascock Memorial Prize for poetry. *The Archive* published many of the poems which were to make up *The Mind's Geography* (1941). On the strength of this volume, Zaturenski was given a Guggenheim Fellowship in 1942-43. The fruit of this fellowship year, spent in Durham, is *Like the Rose* (1945), a book illustrated by Zaturenski's wife, Elizabeth Crowther ('42). He served as instructor in verse and modern poetry at Black Mountain College, North Carolina, for a year. He is now Poet in Residence at Marietta College, Marietta, Ohio. Mrs. Zaturenski is Artist in Residence at the same institution.

The following illustrated and designed the book under the direction of CLARE LEIGHTON: MARY DOMINICK, '47, of Swarthmore, Pennsylvania; LORING FOUNTAIN, '47, of Sherman Oaks, California; WINIFRED GRIMES, '47, of Pittsburgh, Pennsylvania; MARGARET JENKINS, '46, of Salisbury; MARGARET JEAN MERKER, '48, of East Orange, New Jersey; JANE MERIWETHER, '46, of Kansas City, Missouri; KATHERINE ANN MORRISON, '48, of St. Petersburg, Florida; JANE NORR, '47, of Durham; JOSEPHINE ALLEN PARTY (A.B., '44), of Elizabethton, Tennessee; BARBARA PERKINS, '46, of Rutland, Vermont; JEAN LOUISE VERNER, '46, of Miami, Florida; ANN WATSON, of Durham; ANKE ZENER (Mrs. KARL ZENER), of Durham.

Index

PAGE

Illustrations by

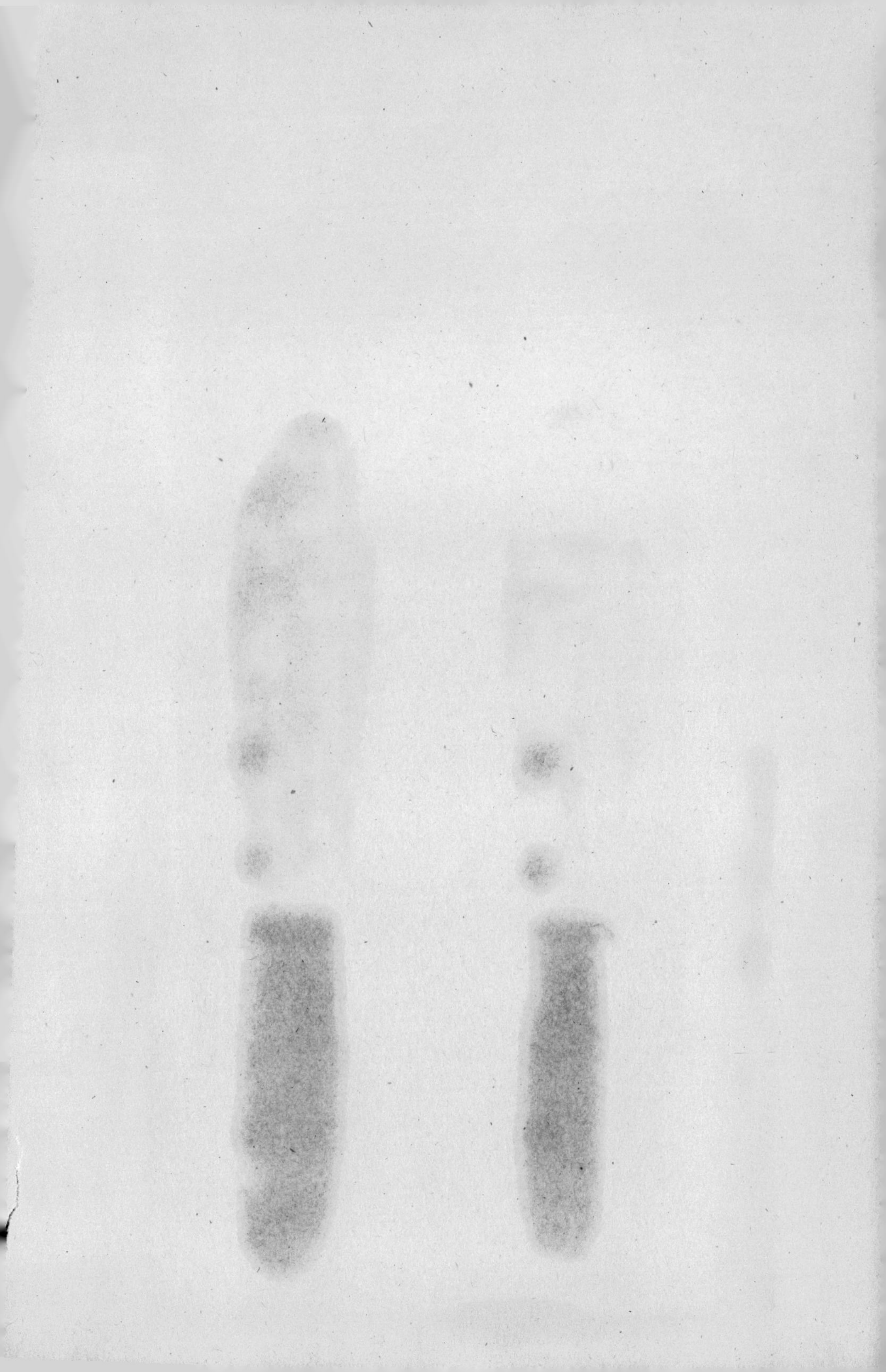